NEW Keystone C

WORKBOOK

NEW
Keystone C

Workbook

Copyright © 2019 by Pearson Education, Inc.

All rights reserved. No part of this publication may be reproduced, stored in a retrieval system, or transmitted in any form or by any means, electronic, mechanical, photocopying, recording, or otherwise, without the prior permission of the publisher.

Pearson, 221 River Street, Hoboken, NJ 07030

Cover Credit: Sergii Mostovyi/123RF

ISBN-10: 0-13-523379-8
ISBN-13: 978-0-13-523379-5

Contents

Unit 1

Reading 1
Vocabulary: Key Words 1
Vocabulary: Academic Words 2
Word Study: Double Consonants 3
Reading Strategy: Preview 4
Comprehension 5
Extension 5
Grammar: Sequence Words and Phrases; Appositives 6
Writing: Describe an Event or Experience 8

Reading 2
Vocabulary: Key Words 9
Vocabulary: Academic Words 10
Word Study: Nouns That Modify Nouns 11
Reading Strategy: Recognize Sequence 12
Comprehension 13
Extension 13
Grammar: Simple Past: Regular and Irregular Verbs 14
Writing: Describe an Object 16

Reading 3
Vocabulary: Literary Words 17
Vocabulary: Academic Words 18
Word Study: Apostrophes 19
Reading Strategy: Visualize 20
Comprehension 21
Response to Literature 21
Grammar: Comparison Structures: Adjectives and Adverbs 22
Writing: Describe a Place 24

Writing Workshop 25
Learning Log 26
Test Preparation 27
Visual Literacy: Smithsonian American Art Museum 31

Contents

Unit 2

Reading 1
Vocabulary: Key Words 33
Vocabulary: Academic Words 34
Word Study: Words with *ch* and *tch* 35
Reading Strategy: Recognize Cause and Effect 36
Comprehension 37
Extension. 37
Grammar: Simple and Compound Sentences 38
Writing: Write a Story with a Starter 40

Reading 2
Vocabulary: Literary Words 41
Vocabulary: Academic Words 42
Word Study: Prefixes *im-*, *over-*, *un-*, *after-* 43
Reading Strategy: Identify Problems and Solutions 44
Comprehension 45
Response to Literature. 45
Grammar: Gerunds as Subjects and Subject Complements; Gerunds as Objects 46
Writing: Rewrite a Familiar Story 48

Reading 3
Vocabulary: Literary Words 49
Vocabulary: Academic Words 50
Word Study: Closed Compound Nouns 51
Reading Strategy: Predict 52
Comprehension 53
Response to Literature. 53
Grammar: Passive: Simple Past; Regular and Irregular Past Participles;
   Passive Forms of the Verb: Review 54
Writing: Write a Personal Narrative 56

Writing Workshop 57
Learning Log 58
Test Preparation 59
Visual Literacy: Smithsonian American Art Museum 63

Contents

Unit 3

Reading 1
Vocabulary: Literary Words 65
Vocabulary: Academic Words 66
Word Study: Spelling -s Blends 67
Reading Strategy: Recognize Cultural Context 68
Comprehension 69
Response to Literature 69
Grammar: Imperatives; Embedded Questions 70
Writing: Write Instructions 72

Reading 2
Vocabulary: Key Words 73
Vocabulary: Academic Words 74
Word Study: Suffixes -er, -or 75
Reading Strategy: Compare and Contrast 76
Comprehension 77
Extension 77
Grammar: Complex Sentences; Agreement in Complex Sentences 78
Writing: Write a Critique 80

Reading 3
Vocabulary: Literary Words 81
Vocabulary: Academic Words 82
Word Study: Synonyms 83
Reading Strategy: Identify with a Character 84
Comprehension 85
Response to Literature 85
Grammar: Transitions; Adjectives 86
Writing: Write to Compare and Contrast 88

Writing Workshop 89
Learning Log 90
Test Preparation 91
Visual Literacy: Smithsonian American Art Museum 95

Contents

Unit 4

Reading 1
Vocabulary: Key Words 97
Vocabulary: Academic Words 98
Word Study: Silent Letters 99
Reading Strategy: Use Visuals 100
Comprehension 101
Extension 101
Grammar: Adjectival Clauses; Subject and Object Relative Pronouns 102
Writing: Write a Magazine Article 104

Reading 2
Vocabulary: Literary Words 105
Vocabulary: Academic Words 106
Word Study: Homophones 107
Reading Strategy: Summarize 108
Comprehension 109
Response to Literature 109
Grammar: Adjectives and Adjectival Phrases; Adverbs and Adverbial Phrases 110
Writing: Write a Plot Summary 112

Reading 3
Vocabulary: Literary Words 113
Vocabulary: Academic Words 114
Word Study: Spelling Long *o* 115
Reading Strategy: Analyze Text Structure 1 116
Comprehension 117
Response to Literature 117
Grammar: Adverbial Clauses 118
Writing: Write a Response to Literature 120

Writing Workshop 121
Learning Log 122
Test Preparation 123
Visual Literacy: Smithsonian American Art Museum 127

Contents

Unit 5

Reading 1
Vocabulary: Key Words 129
Vocabulary: Academic Words 130
Word Study: Capitalization 131
Reading Strategy: Identify Main Idea and Details 132
Comprehension 133
Extension 133
Grammar: Inseparable Phrasal Verbs; Separable Phrasal Verbs 134
Writing: Write a Letter to the Editor 136

Reading 2
Vocabulary: Literary Words 137
Vocabulary: Academic Words 138
Word Study: Antonyms 139
Reading Strategy: Read Aloud 140
Comprehension 141
Response to Literature 141
Grammar: Present and Past Perfect; Factual and Unreal Conditionals ... 142
Writing: Write a Persuasive Paragraph 144

Reading 3
Vocabulary: Literary Words 145
Vocabulary: Academic Words 146
Word Study: Words Ending with Consonant + -le, -al, -el 147
Reading Strategy: Make Inferences 148
Comprehension 149
Response to Literature 149
Grammar: Quoted Speech and Reported Speech; Present Perfect Progressive ... 150
Writing: Write a Review 152

Writing Workshop 153
Learning Log 154
Test Preparation 155
Visual Literacy: Smithsonian American Art Museum 159

Contents

Unit 6

Reading 1
Vocabulary: Literary Words 161
Vocabulary: Academic Words 162
Word Study: Spelling Long *i* 163
Reading Strategy: Read for Enjoyment 164
Comprehension 165
Response to Literature 165
Grammar: Prepositions; More about Antecedent / Pronoun Agreement;
   Capitalization and Punctuation of Titles; Punctuation: Hyphens and Dashes 166
Writing: Include Paraphrases and Citations 170

Reading 2
Vocabulary: Literary Words 171
Vocabulary: Academic Words 172
Word Study: Lexical Sets 173
Reading Strategy: Analyze Text Structure and Elements of Poetry 174
Comprehension 175
Response to Literature 175
Grammar: Expressions of Quantity: *both, either, neither*; Parallel Structure;
   Punctuation: Semicolons and Colons 176
Writing: Write an Introductory Paragraph 180

Reading 3
Vocabulary: Key Words 181
Vocabulary: Academic Words 182
Word Study: Acronyms 183
Reading Strategy: Take Notes 184
Comprehension 185
Extension 185
Grammar: More Transitions; Present and Past Progressive; Parentheses,
   Brackets, and Ellipses; Quoting Sources 186
Writing: Include Quotations and Citations 190

Writing Workshop 191
Learning Log 192
Test Preparation 193
Visual Literacy: Smithsonian American Art Museum 197

Name _____ Date _____

UNIT 1 How can change improve people's lives?

Reading 1: "What's for Dinner?"

Vocabulary Key Words *Use with Student Edition page 5.*

Write each word in the box next to its definition.

| advantages | developed | disadvantages | produce | shipped | traits |

Example: __shipped__ : sent from one location to another

1. _____ : made more complete or advanced

2. _____ : unfavorable conditions

3. _____ : characteristics, usually referring to that of a living thing

4. _____ : to make or manufacture

5. _____ : favorable conditions

Use the words in the box at the top of the page to complete the sentences.

6. The snow conditions in the mountains presented _____ for the hiking trip.

7. The store _____ the sale items to the shoppers who could not come in person.

8. Our dog has _____ that make him look similar to the neighbor's dog.

9. The artist can't _____ enough paintings to meet the demand at the art show.

10. The storm clouds _____ over the baseball field just as the game began.

11. Students who study for tests have _____ over those who do not study.

Unit 1 • Reading 1   1

Vocabulary — Academic Words *Use with Student Edition page 6.*

Read the paragraph below. Pay attention to the underlined Academic Words.

> Scientists have <u>achieved</u> success in genetically engineering many different kinds of food. One famous example is Golden Rice. Scientists used genes to add Vitamin A to the rice, which helps prevent blindness in children. However, people have different <u>attitudes</u> about genetically modified foods. Where some people see great scientific <u>advances</u> and benefits, others fear that these foods are a danger. In some countries, genetically modified foods are even <u>illegal</u>.

Write the Academic Words from the paragraph above next to their correct definitions.

1. _____: succeeded in doing something, especially by working hard
2. _____: not allowed by law
3. _____: thoughts or feelings about something or someone
4. _____: developments or improvements

Use the Academic Words from the paragraph above to complete the sentences.

5. It is _____ to drive without a driver's license.
6. Different people have different _____ about politics.
7. Many _____ in medicine have saved lives.
8. She worked hard all her life and _____ great things.

Complete the sentences with your own ideas.

Example: In the past, _____*my ancestors*_____ suffered from discrimination.

9. Recent advances in technology include _____.
10. My attitude toward _____ has changed over time.
11. _____ achieved wonderful things in life.
12. I know that it is illegal to _____.

Name _____ Date _____

Word Study — Double Consonants *Use with Student Edition page 7.*

REMEMBER When an ending is added to a single-syllable word that ends in a vowel + a consonant, the final consonant is doubled, as in *spin/spinning*. If the word has more than one syllable, the consonant is doubled if the stress is on the final syllable, as in *control/controlling*.

Add an ending as directed to each word. Write the word in the last column.

Base Word	+ Ending	= New Word
hop	-ed	hopped
1. sit	-ing	
2. submit	-ed	
3. pat	-ed	
4. snap	-ing	
5. shop	-ing	

Create a new word by adding the ending *-ed* or *-ing* to each word below.

Example: begin + ___ing___ = ___beginning___

6. fasten + _____ = _____

7. spot + _____ = _____

8. omit + _____ = _____

9. slip + _____ = _____

10. clap + _____ = _____

Unit 1 • Reading 1

Reading Strategy | **Preview**

Use with Student Edition page 7.

REMEMBER Preview the text before reading it by looking at the title, headings, and any visuals. Read the first and last sentences of each paragraph. Ask yourself about the topic to see what you know already. Previewing helps you set a purpose for reading.

Look at the article below and answer the questions that follow.

Mountainous Region of the Western United States of America

Mountain Ranges

The Western United States of America is home to several mountain ranges. They span the states Colorado to California and Montana to New Mexico. People travel to the mountains to climb, camp and ski. Some visitors go just for the beautiful views and the clear mountain air.

The Sierra Nevada, Cascade and Coastal Ranges spread across the west coast of the United States and into Mexico and Canada.

The Rocky, Sierra Nevada, Cascade and Coastal Ranges

The Rocky Mountain Range spans over 2000 miles from Mexico to the U.S. state of Alaska. It is made up of over 100 smaller mountain ranges. The highest peak in the range is near Leadville, Colorado.

1. Read the title and headings. What do you think the article is going to be about?

   _____

2. What does the picture tell you about the topic of the article?

   _____

3. Read the first and last sentences in each paragraph. What more did you learn about the article?

   _____

4. What do you already know about the topic?

   _____

5. How can previewing help you understand an article?

   _____

Comprehension *Use with Student Edition page 14.*

Choose the best answer for each item. Circle the letter of the correct answer.

1. One of the biggest changes in modern food is _____.

   a. price b. transportation c. appearance

2. Farmers began breeding two different varieties of plants together to create _____.

   a. nutrients b. genes c. hybrids

3. The first watermelons were grown in _____.

   a. Africa b. Asia c. the Americas

4. The physical traits of plants and animals are determined by _____.

   a. pesticides b. deficiencies c. genes

5. An advantage to hydroponic farming is that it _____.

   a. saves water and space b. grows food more cheaply c. requires more soil

Extension *Use with Student Edition page 15.*

Write a short paragraph describing how you think food will be grown and consumed in the future. Will there be enough food for everyone? Will we be eating different foods than today? Will there still be farms?

_____
_____
_____
_____
_____
_____
_____
_____
_____

Unit 1 • Reading 1

Grammar — Sequence Words and Phrases

Use with Student Edition page 16.

REMEMBER Sequencing words and phrases such as *first, then, next, after that, now, finally,* and *last* describe the order in which events take place. *First* introduces the first thing that happened; *finally* and *last* introduce the last thing; *then, next, after that,* and *now* introduce anything that happened in between. Most of these sequencing words and phrases take a comma after them, but *then* and *now* do not.
Be sure to use parallel structure and consistent verb tense when narrating a sequence of events.

Put the events for making a collage in the correct order. Then choose an appropriate sequencing word from the box. Be sure to use commas when necessary.

| Last | Next | Then | After that | Now | ~~First~~ |

1. _____ I cut out the pictures. _____
2. _____ I arranged the pictures on the construction paper. _____
3. _____ I got a piece of construction paper and some glue. _____
4. _____ I chose about 20 pictures from the magazines. _____
5. _____ I glued the pictures on the construction paper. _____
6. _____First_____, I collected some magazines. __/__

Tell a brief story, give instructions, or give directions using sequencing words. You may write it in the form of a list or a paragraph. Be sure to use commas when necessary.

_____
_____
_____
_____
_____
_____
_____

Name _____ Date _____

Grammar — Appositives *Use with Student Edition page 17.*

REMEMBER An appositive is a noun or noun phrase that renames another noun. An appositive appears near the noun it renames. A nonrestrictive appositive gives extra information about the noun, and a comma or dash is used to set off the appositive. A restrictive appositive gives essential information, and no comma or dash is used.

Underline the appositive in each sentence. Write *R* if the appositive is restrictive or *N* if it is nonrestrictive. Then circle the noun or noun phrase that the appositive renames.

Example: (The clown), a professional entertainer, performed at my party. __N__

1. I saw the most magnificent animal, a white-tailed deer, at the park. _____

2. My sister Ava became a nurse after she graduated. _____

3. St. Petersburg, a city of almost five million people, was designed by Peter the Great. _____

4. The U.S. president John Kennedy was known for his speaking skills. _____

5. My brother's car, a red Volkswagen, broke down this morning. _____

6. My friend Bill called me last night. _____

7. A friendly and beautiful tabby, Sam, was my favorite cat. _____

8. My cousin Ye Won lives in South Korea. _____

Unit 1 • Reading 1

Writing — **Describe an Event or Experience**

Use with Student Edition pages 18–19.

Complete your own sequence-of-events organizer about an exciting event you participated in or attended.

First

↓

Next

↓

Then

↓

Finally

Use the Peer Review Checklist below to obtain feedback from your partner. This feedback will help you edit your final draft.

Peer Review Checklist

- ☐ Does the first sentence introduce the main idea?
- ☐ Is the description organized chronologically?
- ☐ Did the writer use sequence words to make the sequence clear?
- ☐ Does the writer include details to make each step of the description vivid?
- ☐ Does the concluding sentence sum up the experience?
- ☐ What changes could be made to improve the paragraph?

Name _____ Date _____

How can change improve people's lives?

Reading 2: "Early Inventions"

Vocabulary — **Key Words** *Use with Student Edition page 21.*

Write each word in the box next to its definition.

| emergency | device | idea | identical | invention | patent |

Example: __device__ : a machine or other small object that does a special job

1. _____ : exactly the same as something else

2. _____ : something new that is made for the first time

3. _____ : a serious or dangerous situation

4. _____ : a document that says you have the right to make or sell an invention

5. _____ : a thought or suggestion

Use the words in the box at the top of the page to complete the sentences.

6. The campers brought extra food and water with them in case there is an _____.

7. She built a _____ out of some old machine parts in her basement.

8. Our study group had the best _____ for the class presentation.

9. The engineer applied for a _____ to protect his new _____.

10. The artist was asked to make the same drawing for both rooms, so they had to be _____.

Vocabulary — **Academic Words** *Use with Student Edition page 22.*

Read the paragraph below. Pay attention to the underlined Academic Words.

> In March 2007, a boat <u>created</u> by a Swiss company made history by sailing across the Atlantic Ocean. The boat had solar panels on its roof whose <u>function</u> was to collect sunlight. This <u>technology</u> allowed the boat to cross the Atlantic using only solar energy. The journey proved that the sun can be a <u>significant</u> source of energy.

Write the letter of the correct definition next to each word.

Example: __b__ function   a. made or invented

____ 1. significant   b. the purpose of something

____ 2. technology   c. noticeable or important

____ 3. created   d. all the knowledge and equipment used in science

Use the Academic Words from the exercise above to complete the sentences.

4. The machine is very complicated, but its _____ is not clear.

5. New _____ allows people to travel and communicate in new ways.

6. The invention of the printing press was a _____ event.

7. The painter _____ a beautiful new work of art for the gallery.

Complete the sentences with your own ideas.

Example: I think that new technology has made __communication much easier__.

8. One important function of a fence around a yard is to

_____.

9. Once my friends and I created a(n) _____.

10. I spend a significant amount of time on _____.

10   Unit 1 • Reading 2

Name _____ Date _____

Word Study   Nouns that Modify Nouns

Use with Student Edition page 23.

> **REMEMBER** A noun names a person, place, thing, or idea. Sometimes a noun can function as an adjective to modify (describe) another noun. For example, *piano* is a noun because it names an object. In the phrase *piano music*, *piano* is an adjective because it modifies the noun *music*. Knowing that a noun can modify a noun helps you use words correctly.

Read each sentence. Then circle the noun modifier and underline the noun being modified.

Example: They ate their (evening) meal.

1. We have a new grocery store in the neighborhood.
2. They sell good breakfast cereal.
3. I like fruit drinks because they are healthful.
4. The package design really gets your attention.
5. You can learn a lot from television advertisements.

Add a noun to modify each noun to complete each sentence.

Example: Charles makes ____potato____ soup.

6. Matt got a _____ puppy.
7. Wren uses too much _____ spray.
8. The _____ towel has a beautiful pattern.
9. Rico buys a _____ ring.
10. The dog likes to chew _____ toys.

Unit 1 • Reading 2

Reading Strategy: Recognize Sequence

Use with Student Edition page 23.

REMEMBER Recognizing sequence helps you understand the order in which things happen. Look for words that show sequence, such as *first, then, next, finally, last, while, during,* and *after*. Look for dates and times.

Read the paragraph and answer the questions that follow.

Bessie Coleman

On June 15, 1921, Bessie Coleman became the first African-American woman to earn a pilot's license. She got her license in France. Then she returned to the United States and participated in flight shows. In the 1920s, flight shows were one of the few ways that pilots could make a living flying. During this time, Bessie became a figure in the media because she was a woman and an African American who had a pilot's license. She also performed daring stunts.

Although she liked her work and her new-found fame, the next thing she wanted to do was open a flight school for African Americans. Sadly, Bessie died in a plane accident before realizing her dream. But her bravery has inspired many people to pursue their dreams no matter what the obstacles.

1. What is the first event that happens in the passage?

   _____

2. What is the next event that happens in the passage?

   _____

3. What did Coleman do while she was a pilot?

   _____

4. What is the final event described by the passage?

   _____

5. How can understanding the order of events help you when reading a story?

   _____

Comprehension — *Use with Student Edition page 28.*

Choose the best answer for each item. Circle the letter of the correct answer.

1. The inventor of roller skates was from _____.

   a. England   b. Japan   c. Belgium

2. The first operation under general anesthesia was performed using _____.

   a. newly invented drugs   b. traditional ingredients   c. sound and light

3. Some of the first people to eat canned foods were _____.

   a. children   b. soldiers   c. manufacturers

4. Mary Anderson was inspired to invent windshield wipers while she was _____.

   a. driving an old car   b. watching a bus in the rain   c. riding a streetcar

5. Gideon Sundback developed the modern zipper by _____.

   a. improving earlier inventions   b. creating something entirely new   c. stealing someone else's idea

Extension — *Use with Student Edition page 29.*

Choose five objects that you use today. Research each object to find when and where it was invented. Fill in the chart below.

Object	Origin
pencil	England, 1600s

Unit 1 • Reading 2

Grammar — Simple Past: Regular Verbs

Use with Student Edition page 30.

REMEMBER Form negatives with *did not* (*didn't*) and begin questions with *did*. If the answer to a simple past question is the subject of the sentence, use the affirmative form of the verb.
Example: Who *invented* bubble gum? NOT Who *did invent* bubble gum?

Complete each sentence below with the simple past of the verb in parentheses.

Example: Inventions (transform) __transformed__ society.

1. My grandmother always (dry) _____ her laundry on a clothesline.

2. We (want) _____ to go swimming, but the pool (close) _____ at five.

3. They (try) _____ to invent a new way to communicate.

4. He (not live) _____ in Paris for very long before he (move) _____.

Complete the following simple past questions with the verb in parentheses. Then answer in complete sentences, using information from the reading.

Example: What *did* you *do* last night? (do)
Last night I studied and watched TV.

1. What time _____ you _____ at school? (arrive)
   _____

2. When _____ you _____ studying English? (start)
   _____

3. Where _____ you _____ on your last vacation? (visit)
   _____

4. What _____ you _____ last weekend? (do)
   _____

Name _____ Date _____

Grammar **Simple Past: Irregular Verbs**

Use with Student Edition page 31.

> **REMEMBER** The simple past forms of many common verbs are irregular. You must memorize these. The negative of irregular verbs is formed the same way as the negative of regular verbs, with *did not (didn't)*. Questions begin with *did*. The simple past of the verb *be* is *was* or *were*. The negative is *wasn't* or *weren't*. Questions begin with *was* or *were*.

Complete each sentence below with the simple past of the verb in parentheses.

Example: He (put) _____put_____ his jeans in the washing machine.

1. She (know) _____ the answer to the question.

2. There (be) _____ problems with the first transatlantic cable.

3. They (throw) _____ me a surprise party.

4. He (not be) _____ happy about how he (do) _____ on the test.

Complete the following simple past questions with the verb in parentheses. Then answer them in complete sentences, using information from the reading.

Example: What time *did* you *go* to bed last night? (go)
 Last night I went to bed at 10:30.

5. What _____ you _____ for breakfast? (make)

   _____

6. What time _____ you _____ to school today? (come)

   _____

7. What _____ you _____ to school today? (bring)

   _____

8. What _____ your parents _____ you this morning? (tell)

   _____

Writing — **Describe an Object** *Use with Student Edition pages 32-33.*

Complete your own word web for a paragraph about an object that you have used, eaten, or worn.

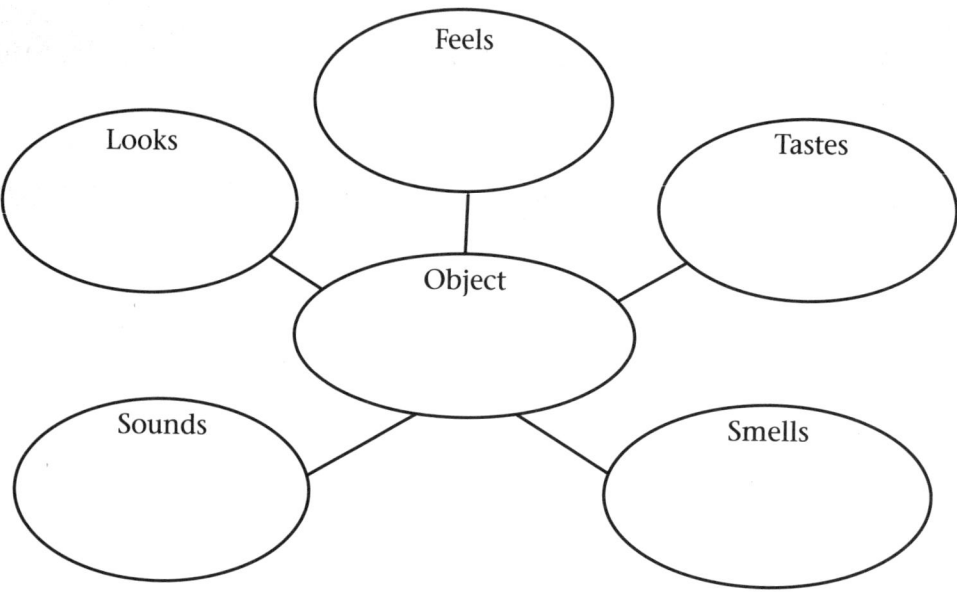

Use the Peer Review Checklist below to obtain feedback from your partner. This feedback will help you edit your final draft.

Peer Review Checklist

- ☐ Is the main topic of the description clear?
- ☐ Does the writer include sensory details to describe the object?
- ☐ Does the paragraph give the reader a vivid picture of the writer's experience?
- ☐ Does the writer use a variety of verbs and adverbs to make the description vivid?
- ☐ Are verbs in the simple past used correctly?
- ☐ What changes could be made to improve the paragraph?

Name _____ Date _____

How can change improve people's lives?

Reading 3: "Milkweeds from Nevaeh"

Vocabulary Literary Words Use with Student Edition page 35.

REMEMBER **Imagery** is descriptive language used in literary works. Imagery is created by using sensory details. **Setting** is the time and place of the action of a story. Sensory details help establish the setting in the reader's mind. A **simile** is a comparison between two or more unlike things using the words *like* or *as* to compare them.

Each sentence establishes its setting or action with sensory details. Label each sentence with the sense it refers to: smell, taste, touch, sight, or sound. Circle the simile.

Sense	Description
touch	The hot sand was rough against her feet.
1.	Night had turned the whole town as black as coal.
2.	The fruit drink was too sugary sweet for me.
3.	The evening breeze brought the faint scent of the autumn leaves through the window.

Read the passage below. Then answer the questions.

> The broad leaves high above us were deep green with hints of yellow and red. Thin beams of light touched the soft ground. Colorful tropical birds called out in strange voices. The dirt below us was moist, and small drops of water fell to the ground like petals. Our guide told us to look up, and we saw two monkeys swinging from a branch. They chattered back and forth like people. The air was warm and sweet.

4. What is the setting of the passage? _____

5. List the sensory details that help establish the setting.

_____

_____

6. Which detail is a simile?

_____

Unit 1 • Reading 3

Vocabulary — Academic Words *Use with Student Edition page 36.*

Read the paragraph below. Pay attention to the underlined Academic Words.

> One day my teacher asked our class to come up with a plan to help make our school a more beautiful place. With this <u>goal</u> in mind, I noticed that an old garden bed located next to the parking lot was filled with weeds. In class the next day, I suggested that the class plant a garden there. My teacher and classmates <u>reacted</u> with excitement to my idea. They said I had great <u>insight</u> about what our class needed. The whole class got <u>involved</u> in planning and planting the new garden.

Write the Academic Words from the paragraph above next to their correct definition.

Example: ___insight___: something you realize is very important or meaningful

1. _____: included in a project or situation

2. _____: behaved in a particular way because of what someone has said or done

3. _____: something you want to do in the future

Use the Academic Words from the paragraph above to complete the sentences.

4. The florist had some great _____ about what the community garden meant to everyone.

5. Everyone _____ with shock when the news came.

6. She worked all summer to reach her _____.

7. The whole team was _____ in the project.

Complete the sentences with your own ideas.

Example: By reading that book, I gained some insight about ___Italy___.

8. I reacted to the good news by _____.

9. My family likes to get involved in _____.

10. I have a goal this year to _____.

Unit 1 • Reading 3

Name _____ Date _____

Word Study — Apostrophes *Use with Student Edition page 37.*

> **REMEMBER** An apostrophe (') is used to show possession with a noun. Add *'s* to the end of a singular noun, such as *book of the girl→girl's book*. Add just the apostrophe to the end of a plural noun, such as *books of the girls→girls' books*. An apostrophe is also used to take the place of missing letters in a contraction. For example, *it* and *is* become the contraction *it's*.

Look at the chart below. Form the possessive of each phrase. Write the possessive in the chart.

Phrase	Possessive Form
the ideas of the boy	*the boy's ideas*
1. the suggestion of Dr. Greene	
2. the toys of the child	
3. the strength of the waves	
4. the laughter of Mona	
5. the petals of the flowers	

Look at the chart below. Form the contraction for each pair of words. Write the contraction in the chart.

Word 1	Word 2	Contraction
I	am	*I'm*
6. you	are	
7. is	not	
8. who	is	
9. they	are	
10. he	will	

Unit 1 • Reading 3

Reading Strategy | **Visualize** | *Use with Student Edition page 37.*

REMEMBER When you visualize, you make pictures in your mind of what you are reading.

Read the paragraph and answer the questions that follow.

> I was standing at the edge of the stage, behind the curtain, waiting for my turn in the dance recital. It was an Irish step dance and I was wearing my step shoes, black tights and a green shirt. Last year, I performed in the recital with a group. But this year, it was just me. My palms felt sweaty. I heard my name announced, and I walked out on stage. There I was, on the stage, by myself. The lights were so bright I couldn't see the audience. For a moment, it felt like no one was there. I kept that thought in my head as I danced. It made it seem as if I were performing for a row of lights, not 200 people. My routine seemed effortless. When I finished I heard applause.

1. What is the passage about?

   _____

2. What is the strongest image in the passage?

   _____

3. How do the images help you to make a mental picture of the scene?

   _____

4. Draw a picture of the scene described in the passage. Be sure to include details from the passage in your drawing.

5. How can the skill of visualizing help you to understand a text more clearly?

   _____

Comprehension *Use with Student Edition page 44.*

Choose the best answer for each item. Circle the letter of the correct answer.

1. Jorge calls Nevaeh "my little piece of heaven" because _____.

    a. he loves her name very much
    b. it's the translation of her name
    c. it's her name spelled backwards

2. The community garden was located in a _____.

    a. empty lot   b. downtown park   c. parking lot

3. Hanna said that tomatoes don't like too much _____.

    a. soil   b. water   c. sun

4. Milkweed is the only plant that _____.

    a. Monarch butterflies can eat
    b. Monarch caterpillars won't eat
    c. Monarch larvae will eat

5. At the end of the story, Nevaeh's relationship with her foster parents _____.

    a. has improved   b. is about the same   c. has worsened

Response to Literature *Use with Student Edition page 45.*

Imagine that you live in the neighborhood with Nevaeh, Jorge, Robyn, and Hanna. One day you see someone planting flowers in the vacant lot. What do you feel when you see the person? What will you do next? Will you join the person in the garden? Write a short paragraph to describe the situation.

_____
_____
_____
_____
_____
_____
_____

Unit 1 • Reading 3

Grammar — Comparison Structures: Adjectives

Use with Student Edition page 46.

> **REMEMBER** A comparative adjective + *than* compares two things. *The* + a superlative adjective compares three or more things. For most one-syllable adjectives, form the comparative by adding *-er* and the superlative by adding *-est*. For one-syllable adjectives with a consonant-vowel-consonant pattern, such as *big*, double the last consonant and add *-er/-est*.
> **Example:** This math test is *harder* than last week's. That tomato is the *biggest* one in the market.
> For most two-syllable adjectives ending in *-y*, change the *y* to *i* and add *-er* or *-est*.
> **Example:** My *scariest* experience was two years ago on that roller coaster.
> Add *more* or *most* before most other adjectives of two or more syllables.
> **Example:** The public pool is *more exciting* than the library.
> Some adjectives have irregular forms.
> **Example:** This is the *worst* dress I have tried on today.

Complete each sentence with the correct form of the adjective in parentheses.

Example: (bright) The stars today are ___brighter than___ they were yesterday.

1. (icy) The sidewalk is _____ than the driveway.

2. (serious) He is the _____ student in the class.

3. (good) Broccoli tastes _____ than spinach.

Write sentences with comparative and superlative adjectives. Follow the directions in parentheses.

Example: (Use the superlative form of *large*.)
    That is the largest house in the neighborhood.

4. (Use the comparative form of *intelligent*.)

   _____

5. (Use the superlative form of *strong*.)

   _____

Name _____ Date _____

Grammar   Comparison Structures: Adverbs

Use with Student Edition page 47.

> **REMEMBER** Use comparative and superlative adverbs to compare two actions. For one-syllable adverbs, add *-er* and *-est* to the adverb. For two- or more syllable adverbs and adverbs that end in *-ly*, use *more* and *most* + adverb. Just as with comparative and superlative adjectives, you can use *than* with comparative adverbs and *the* with superlative adverbs. If the comparison is understood, you don't need the *than* clause.
> **Example:** I am doing better now (than I was before).
> Some adverbs are irregular in the comparative and superlative form.
> **Examples:** *well, better, best; badly, worse, worst;* and *far, farther (further), farthest (furthest).*
> Some adverbs have the same form as adjectives.
> **Examples:** *early, hard, late, fast,* and *high.*
> Their comparative and superlative forms are also the same.

Complete each sentence below with the comparative or superlative form of the adverb in parentheses.

Example: I (well) speak English _____**better**_____ now than last year.

1. (politely) She greeted me the _____ out of everyone.

2. (happily) He smiled _____ than before.

3. (badly) Our team played the _____ that we'd ever played.

4. (gracefully) That girl dances the _____ of all.

5. (badly) I have never done _____ than I did on that test.

6. (early) I get up _____ than my brother does.

7. (high) A duck can fly _____ than a chicken can.

8. (hard) Mike works _____ out of anyone in class.

9. (carefully / fast) He drives _____ since he had his accident. He drove much _____ in the past.

10. (quietly) We talked _____ after the children went to bed.

Writing **Describe a Place** *Use with Student Edition pages 48–49.*

Complete your own three-column chart for a paragraph describing a place you are familiar with.

Back	Middle	Front

Use the Peer Review Checklist below to obtain feedback from your partner. This feedback will help you edit your final draft.

Peer Review Checklist
- ☐ Does the paragraph give an overview of the scene?
- ☐ Are the parts of the scene described in spatial order?
- ☐ Is the description organized chronologically?
- ☐ Does the paragraph give the reader a clear picture of the scene?
- ☐ Are comparative and superlative adjectives used correctly?
- ☐ What changes could be made to improve the paragraph?

Name _____ Date _____

Writing Workshop *Use with Student Edition pages 54–57.*

Organize your ideas in the graphic organizer below.

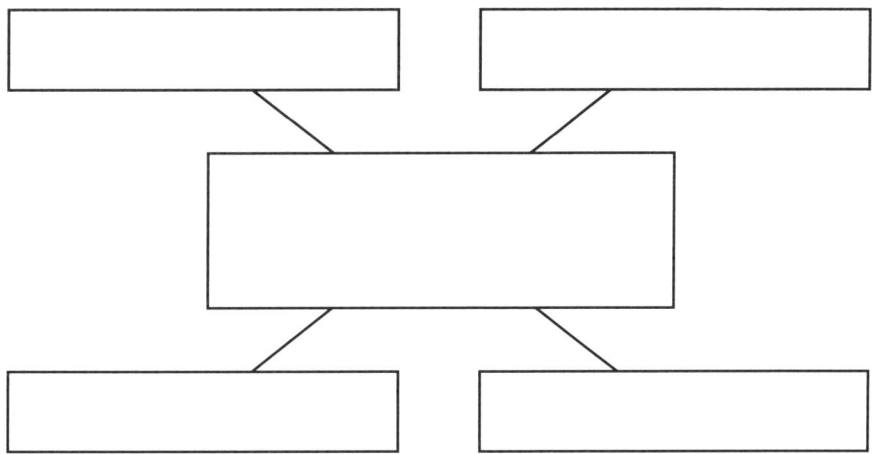

Use the Peer Review Checklist below to obtain feedback from your partner. This feedback will help you edit your final draft.

Peer Review Checklist

- ☐ Does the first paragraph introduce the topic?
- ☐ Does the concluding paragraph sum up the main ideas?
- ☐ Does the essay describe the experience clearly?
- ☐ Is the description organized chronologically?
- ☐ Is there a development in the writer's feelings before and after the experience?
- ☐ Is it clear why the experience changed the writer?
- ☐ What changes could be made to improve the essay?

Learning Log — *Use with Student Edition page 58.*

Underline the vocabulary items you know and can use well. Review and practice any you haven't underlined. Underline them when you know them well.

Literary Words	Key Words	Academic Words	
imagery setting simile	traits advantages disadvantages device emergency identical invention patent	achieved advances attitudes illegal	created function significant technology goal involved insight reacted

Put a check by the skills you can perform well. Review and practice any you haven't checked off. Check them off when you can perform them well.

Skills	I can . . .
Word Study	☐ recognize and spell double consonants. ☐ recognize and use nouns modifying nouns. ☐ use apostrophes.
Reading Strategies	☐ preview. ☐ recognize sequence. ☐ visualize.
Grammar	☐ use sequence words and appositives. ☐ use appositives. ☐ use regular and irregular simple past verbs. ☐ use comparison structures.
Writing	☐ describe an event or experience. ☐ describe an object. ☐ describe a place. ☐ write a descriptive essay.

Name _____ Date _____

Test Preparation

Test 1

DIRECTIONS
Read this selection. Then answer the questions that follow it.

Jing and Sarah are in Mrs. Sampson's class. They have to do a report about where refugees settle in the United States. Jing is very excited when he finds this chart. He thinks it will help them for the report.

Refugee Settlement in 2009

State	Rank	Number of Refugees
Arizona	4	4,320
California	1	11,278
Florida	5	4,193
Michigan	6	3,500
New York	3	4,412
Texas	2	8,212

1 Which state receives the most refugees?
  A Arizona
  B Califonia
  C New York
  D Texas

2 Which state is ranked third?
  A Texas
  B Michigan
  C Florida
  D New York

3 Who wants Sarah to do a report?
  A Jing
  B Her father
  C The class
  D Mrs. Sampson

Test Preparation 27

Test 2

DIRECTIONS
Read this selection. Then answer the questions that follow it.

Hubble Space Telescope

1   Edwin Hubble was an astronomer—a scientist who studied objects in space. Hubble saw that galaxies were moving away from Earth. He guessed that the universe is getting bigger. He formulated a law called Hubble's Law based on this discovery. The Hubble Space Telescope is also named for him.

2   The Hubble Space Telescope was designed in 1970, but it was not launched until 1990. The telescope was launched from the space shuttle Discovery. The telescope orbits Earth and takes pictures, moving at a speed of five miles per second. It completes a journey around the Earth every ninety-seven minutes!

3   The pictures that the Hubble Space Telescope sends back to Earth provide scientists with a clear view of our solar system. In addition, the telescope allows astronomers to see images of many different galaxies.

4   The telescope was designed with the idea that it could be <u>upgraded</u>, or made better, while it was still in orbit. The United States' National Aeronautics and Space Administration (NASA) sends astronauts to service the telescope. They fix problems, replace equipment, and add new equipment. Astronauts have serviced the telescope five times since it was first launched. The last servicing mission was in May 2009.

---

1 According to the selection, how does the Hubble Space Telescope help scientists?
  A It can be upgraded with new technology.
  B It proves Hubble's Law is true.
  C It gives astronauts a chance to visit the telescope.
  D It gives scientists a clear picture of the solar system.

2 What is paragraph 4 mainly about?
  A Servicing the telescope
  B New technology added to the telescope
  C Problems with the telescope
  D The last servicing mission

3 Which words in paragraph 4 help the reader know what *upgraded* means?
  A in orbit
  B made better
  C was designed
  D the idea

4 The author probably wrote this selection to —
  A compare the Hubble Space Telescope to other telescopes
  B encourage people to find out more about the Hubble Space Telescope
  C explain what the Hubble Space Telescope is and what it does
  D describe the pictures the Hubble Space Telescope sends to scientists

Name _____ Date _____

Test 3

DIRECTIONS
Read this selection. Then answer the questions that follow it.

Lee's Lesson

1   Lee looked forward to Saturdays because that was the day he visited his grandmother. Each Saturday Lee and his family drove to Houston, Texas, U.S.A., where they visited his grandmother at her restaurant in Chinatown. During the day they would help Mei in the kitchen or with customers. In the evening they would eat some of her delicious dumplings and listen to her stories.

2   This Saturday was no different. After their meal, Mei sat in her favorite chair. Lee sat beside her. "Have I told you the story of the ruler who wanted to understand the world?" she asked.

3   "No, you haven't," Lee replied. So Mei began her story.

4   The ruler asked his adviser if it was possible to understand the world. In reply, the adviser told the following story:

5   One day, three men were walking together in the forest. They challenged each other to a game. Each man put a blindfold over his eyes.

6   The men encountered an elephant sleeping in the woods. "What is this thing?" wondered the first man. He reached out and touched one of the elephant's legs and said, "This feels rough and thick, and my arms barely go around it. Surely, this is a tree."

7   The second man laughed. "No, you're wrong, my friend," he replied from his position by the elephant's trunk. "My fingers go around it, and it is flexible. See? It can be easily bent. It is a snake."

8   "Silly friends, you're both wrong," responded the third man. He was standing at the elephant's side and touching the elephant's stomach. "This is a long, wide wall," he said. "I'm sure of it."

9   After the story, the adviser turned to the ruler. "So, Sire," concluded the adviser, "think of this story the next time you believe anyone's story about an event."

10   After Mei finished her story, Lee and his family said good-bye and drove home. Lee thought about his grandmother's story. He wondered if the ruler had learned the same lesson he had.

Test Preparation

1. Use this story map to answer the question below.

   Event 1
   | Lee and his family visit his grandmother. |

   Event 2
   | Lee and his family help his grandmother at her restaurant. |

   Event 3
   | Mei tells Lee a story about a ruler who wants to understand the world. |

   Outcome
   | |

   Which of these belongs in the empty box in the story map?
   A Lee learns a lesson from his grandmother's story.
   B Lee and his family stay at Mei's house.
   C The three men tell what they think the elephant is.
   D The ruler in the story learns a lesson.

2. Paragraph 1 is mainly about —
   A Mei's restaurant and her stories
   B Lee and his family
   C why Lee enjoys visiting his grandmother
   D Mei's delicious dumplings

3. In paragraph 7, what words help the reader know what <u>flexible</u> means?
   A go around it
   B a snake
   C easily bent
   D my fingers

4. Which sentence from the story shows how Lee feels about his grandmother?
   A *In the evening they would eat some of her delicious dumplings and listen to her stories.*
   B *Lee looked forward to Saturdays because that was the day he visited his grandmother.*
   C *During the day they would help Mei in the kitchen or with customers.*
   D *Lee thought about his grandmother's story.*

5. By the end of the story, the reader can conclude that Lee —
   A learned a lesson about helping his grandmother
   B learned that helping your family is important to success
   C learned that his grandmother's stories could be funny
   D learned the importance of finding out about the world for yourself

Name _____ Date _____

Visual Literacy: Smithsonian American
Art Museum *Use with Student Edition pages 60–61.*

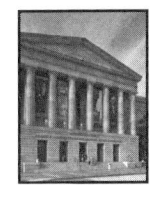

Learning to Look

Look at *Storm King on the Hudson* by Samuel Colman on page 61 in your Student Edition. Place a blank sheet of paper over the right half of the painting. Write down three details that you see on the left side of the painting. State facts, not opinions.

Left Side

Example: _There is smoke from the steamship._

1. _____

2. _____

3. _____

Now move the blank sheet of paper over to cover the left half of the painting. Write down three details that you see on the right side of the painting. State facts, not opinions.

Right Side

4. _____

5. _____

6. _____

Interpretation

Look at *Storm King on the Hudson* again. Imagine a day in the life of the men in the fishing boat on the right side of the painting. What would their day be like? Write your answers below.

Men in Fishing Boat

Example: _It is very hot out here._

_____
_____
_____

Now imagine a day in the life of the men on the steamship on the left side of the painting. What would their day be like? Write your answers below.

Men in Steamship

_____
_____
_____

5W&H

Look at *Fermented Soil* by Hans Hofmann on page 60 in your textbook. Write six questions you would like to ask the artist about this painting.

Example: _What color did you use first?_

1. Who _____
2. Where _____
3. When _____
4. What _____
5. Why _____
6. How _____

Name _____ Date _____

UNIT 2 — What are the benefits of facing challenges?

Reading 1: "Deep Mapping" / "You Can Help the Oceans"

Vocabulary **Key Words** *Use with Student Edition page 65.*

Write each word in the box next to its definition.

| accurate | continuous | data | depth | determine | theory |

Example: __accurate__: correct and exact

1. _____: an idea or system of ideas to explain something

2. _____: distance from the top to bottom of something

3. _____: facts collected to be analyzed

4. _____: to cause something to happen in a particular way

5. _____: without stopping

Use the words in the box at the top of the page to complete the sentences.

6. The scientists collected _____ about the ocean exploration.

7. We can test the scientist's _____ by conducting experiments.

8. The song played in a _____ loop over and over for an hour.

9. It will not be easy to _____ the fastest route to the store.

10. They researched the _____ of the ocean in different locations around the globe.

Unit 2 • Reading 1

Vocabulary — Academic Words *Use with Student Edition page 66.*

Read the paragraph below. Pay attention to the underlined Academic Words.

> During World War II, the United States military wanted to create a <u>code</u> that could not be broken by the enemy. This was a great <u>challenge</u>. The military finally decided to base the code on the language spoken by a Native American tribe, the Navajo. In May of 1942, the first 29 Navajo men came to <u>aid</u> the military. After they helped develop the code, they <u>accompanied</u> the soldiers overseas to help send and receive the secret messages.

Write the letter of the correct definition next to each word.

Example: __d__ accompanied   a. help or support given to someone

_____ 1. aid   b. a way to use words, letters, or numbers to send secret messages

_____ 2. code   c. something difficult that you need skill or ability to do

_____ 3. challenge   d. went somewhere with someone

Use the Academic Words from the exercise above to complete the sentences.

4. My aunt _____ my class on a school trip.

5. Alex and his sister used a secret _____ to pass messages.

6. We expected an easy math test, but it was a major _____.

7. The teacher offered _____ to the students who were falling behind by helping them after class.

Complete the sentences with your own ideas.

Example: My ____best friend____ accompanied me to the park.

8. When I need help, _____ can offer me aid.

9. _____ sends messages in code.

10. I think the biggest challenge I face is _____.

Name _____ Date _____

Word Study Words with *ch* and *tch* *Use with Student Edition page 67.*

REMEMBER In English, the consonant clusters *ch* and *tch* sound the same but are spelled differently. For example: *touch* and *match*. Learning these two patterns can help you spell many words correctly.

Read the words in the box below. Then write each word in the correct column in the chart.

| chain | switch | attach | sketch | latch |
| such | watch | touch | patch | champion |

Words with -*ch*	Words with -*tch*
chain	

Fill in the missing letters in each word. Use *ch* or *tch*. Check your answers in a dictionary.

Example: Mark shouldn't scra __tch__ his mosquito bite!

1. Cleaning my room is one of my _____ ores.

2. I have to do some resear _____ on chimpanzees.

3. Risa has one _____ apter left to read in the novel.

4. On Saturday, I baked a ba _____ of cookies.

5. My favorite vegetables are carrots, peas, and spina _____.

6. We usually stre _____ before and after we exercise.

Unit 2 • Reading 1

Reading Strategy: Recognize Cause and Effect

Use with Student Edition page 67.

> **REMEMBER** Recognizing cause and effect can help you better understand a text. Look for words and phrases such as *because, since, so that, therefore,* and *as a result of.*

Read the paragraph and answer the questions that follow.

> Some students have something called test-taking anxiety. The thought of taking a test can keep them from studying well. This anxiety makes it difficult to concentrate when taking the test. Because of this nervousness, students will do poorly, even though they studied. Psychologists call it test anxiety and offer students tips on dealing with their feelings, so that they can perform better during tests.

1. What is the cause in the paragraph?

   _____

2. What is the effect in the paragraph?

   _____

Read the paragraph and answer the questions that follow.

> Javan was excited about going camping. He became disappointed when the bus had to stop at the bridge. The river was high and flooded the bridge, so they couldn't get across to the campgrounds. As a result, the group got off the bus and crossed the river on foot in a place where the water was low. They hiked the rest of the way to the campsite.

3. What is the cause in the paragraph?

   _____

4. What is the effect in the paragraph?

   _____

5. How might the skill of identifying cause and effect help you when reading the text?

   _____

   _____

Name _____ Date _____

Comprehension
Use with Student Edition page 74.

Choose the *best* answer for each item. Circle the letter of the correct answer.

1. Marie Tharp and Bruce Heezen's main goal was to _____.

   a. map the ocean floor   b. locate the deepest part of the ocean   c. invent new ways to explore the ocean

2. Marie Tharp's work was so unique at the time because she _____.

   a. was a female scientist   b. worked harder than Heezen   c. had no data to work with

3. Tharp and Heezen used new technology that utilized _____ to measure distance.

   a. light   b. water   c. echoes

4. Tharp and Heezen's data was used to make a map that was later _____.

   a. painted   b. photographed   c. explored by submarine

5. Before Tharp and Heezen's mapping, scientists used the theory of _____ to learn about the ocean.

   a. echo sounding   b. the ocean floor   c. continental drift

Extension
Use with Student Edition page 75.

To help you write an article about Marie Tharp's achievements, record your answers to the 5Ws: *Who? What? Where? When? Why?* Look at examples of news headlines and use them to guide you as you write your own articles.

_____
_____
_____
_____
_____
_____
_____
_____

Unit 2 • Reading 1

Grammar Simple and Compound Sentences

Use with Student Edition page 76.

> **REMEMBER** A **simple sentence** contains a subject and a predicate. The predicate tells what the subject does. A predicate always has a verb. **Example:** I walk my dog after school.
> A **compound sentence** has two simple sentences joined by a coordinating conjunction (*and, but,* or *so*), so it often has two verbs. Use a comma before the conjunction that joins the two sentences.
> **Example:** I swim after school, and sometimes I play soccer.
> Remember that *and* connects two ideas, *but* contrasts two ideas, and *so* shows a result.

Write *simple* if a sentence is simple. Write *compound* if it is compound.

_____ 1. Birds and butterflies fly south in the fall.

_____ 2. The sun rises in the east, and it sets in the west.

_____ 3. Spending time in the woods and by the ocean teaches you about nature.

_____ 4. Dragonflies migrate, but they fly in only one direction.

_____ 5. I became interested in Gary Paulsen, so now I want to read more of his books.

Write compound sentences by adding the coordinating conjunction in parentheses and a simple sentence.

Example: (and) Bees were buzzing, _and in the distance a crow was cawing._

6. (but) They planted a garden, _____

7. (and) She went for a walk in the woods, _____

8. (so) Tomorrow he will build a tree house, _____

9. (so) It was getting cold, _____

10. (but) It has not rained all week, _____

38   Unit 2 • Reading 1

Name _____ Date _____

Grammar — Agreement in Simple and Compound Sentences

Use with Student Edition page 77.

> **REMEMBER** In simple sentences and in both independent clauses in compound sentences, the verbs must agree in number with their subjects. For example, if the subject is a plural noun or pronoun (*the boys, them,* etc.), the verb must be plural (*take, were,* etc.). Pronouns must agree with their antecedent, which is the noun that precedes the pronouns that refer to it. For example, if the antecedent is singular and feminine (*the girl, Anna,* etc.), the pronouns that follow must be singular and feminine (*she, hers,* etc.).

Rewrite the sentences, correcting the errors in verb agreement and antecedent-pronoun agreement.

Example: The boys has finished my homework.

The boys have finished their homework.

1. Our teacher don't like noisy students. She make him leave class.

   _____

2. The pony haven't eaten today, and they are hungry.

   _____

3. My head hurt, so she took some medicine.

   _____

4. Ben go to a private school, but her sister go to a public school.

   _____

5. We doesn't have a new car, but they is good enough for me.

   _____

6. The television were broken, so I played a game.

   _____

Unit 2 • Reading 1

Writing: Write a Story with a Starter

Use with Student Edition pages 78–79.

Complete your own word web with details for a fictional narrative beginning with the story starter: *The view was unlike anything I had ever seen before.*

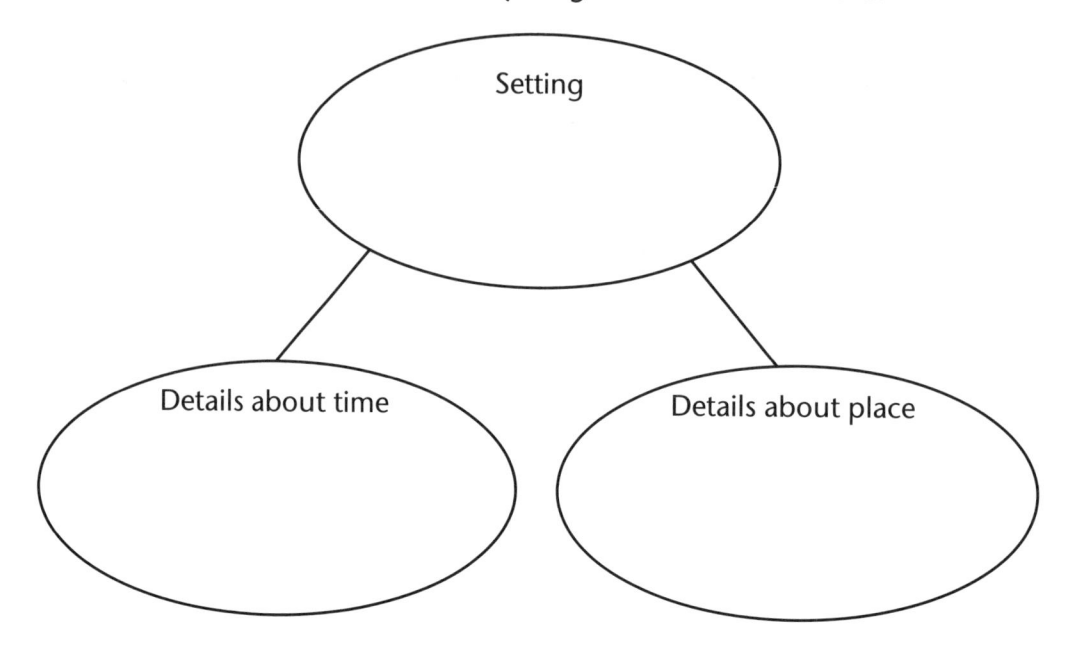

- Setting
  - Details about time
  - Details about place

Have your partner complete (√) the Peer Review Checklist. Use this feedback to help you edit your final draft.

Peer Review Checklist

- ☐ Does the paragraph have a clear setting?
- ☐ Is the setting specific and believable?
- ☐ Does the writer describe the place and the time?
- ☐ Is the paragraph an interesting story starter? Does it make you want to read more?
- ☐ Are simple and compound sentences used correctly?
- ☐ Do the sentences have the correct subject-verb and pronoun agreement?
- ☐ What changes could be made to improve the paragraph?

Name _____ Date _____

UNIT 2: What are the benefits of facing challenges?

Reading 2: "Five New Words at a Time" / "Quilt"

Vocabulary — **Literary Words** *Use with Student Edition page 81.*

> **REMEMBER** Characters are the people or animals involved in a story. Stories are told from the **point of view** of a character or narrator. When you are reading a story, it is important to know who is telling the story. The story is told from that character's point of view. Words such as *I, our,* and *us* normally indicate a *first-person* point of view. An author's memoirs or diaries use the first-person point of view. Words such as *he, she,* and *they* normally indicate a *third-person* point of view. If someone who isn't in the story is telling it, the third-person point of view is used.

Label each sentence with the point of view that is used. Write the name of the character.

Point of View / Character	Sentence
third person / Norman	Norman went to the party.
1.	"Are we going?" my friend asked.
2.	"I'm tired, too," I replied.
3.	We sat down and tried to think of an answer.

Write a sentence for each character and point of view.

Character / Point of View	Sentence
Meredith: first person	I sang the song with a smile.
4. Samuel: third person	
5. the team: first person	

Unit 2 • Reading 2   41

Vocabulary — **Academic Words** *Use with Student Edition page 82.*

Read the paragraph below. Pay attention to the underlined Academic Words.

> Maria is my French pen pal. We <u>communicate</u> mainly through email. I write to her in French, and she writes to me in English. It's exciting when I get a <u>response</u> from her. We <u>approach</u> learning a foreign language in similar ways. We both like reading and writing, and we also enjoy using <u>resources</u> such as language CDs and videos to help with listening and pronunciation.

Write the Academic Words from the paragraph above next to their correct definitions.

Example: __response__: something that is said, written, or done as a reaction or reply to something else

1. _____: a supply of materials used to complete a task

2. _____: express your thoughts or feelings so other people understand them

3. _____: a way of doing something or dealing with a problem

Use the Academic Words from the paragraph above to complete the sentences.

4. The _____ to your letter can be found in today's newspaper.

5. Yu-Lan always used school _____, such as the library and computers.

6. I usually _____ by email with my friend in Germany.

7. We tried a new _____ to solve the problem.

Complete the sentences with your own ideas.

Example: I approach tough projects __slowly and carefully__.

8. I got a positive response when I asked my friends to _____.

9. I communicate with friends by _____.

10. Some useful resources in my town are _____.

Name _____ Date _____

Word Study — Prefixes *im-, over-, un-, after-*

Use with Student Edition page 83.

REMEMBER A **prefix** is a letter or group of letters added to the beginning of a word to change its meaning. For example, the prefixes *im-* and *un-* mean "not." When you add *im-* to the word *possible*, the new word is *impossible*, the opposite of *possible*. Knowing just a few prefixes can help you figure out many unfamiliar words.

Look at the chart below. Add the prefixes *im-, over-, un-,* or *after-* as directed to create a new word. Write the new word on the chart. Then write the meaning.

Base Word	Prefix	New Word	Definition
balance	im-	imbalance	not balanced
1. patient	im-		
2. estimate	over-		
3. flow	over-		
4. even	un-		
5. healthy	un-		
6. thought	after-		
7. shock	after-		

Create a new word by adding the prefix *im-, over-, un-,* or *after-* to each word below. Write the definition next to the new word. Check a dictionary if needed.

Examples: heat overheat heat to excess

8. taste _____

9. steady _____

10. effect _____

11. measurable _____

12. pay _____

13. believable _____

14. mature _____

15. look _____

Unit 2 • Reading 2

Reading Strategy | Identify Problems and Solutions

Use with Student Edition page 83.

> **REMEMBER** When you find the problems and solutions in a text, you will understand it better.

Read the paragraph and answer the questions that follow.

> Hannah could see that her dog, Fergus, was thirsty and hot from running in the summer sun, but she'd forgotten to bring water. She was warned that he might get overheated. Hannah made Fergus lie down, but that didn't help. Then she remembered there was a creek at the edge of the park. She took Fergus to the creek where he could get a drink of water.

1. What is the problem in the passage?

   _____

2. What is the solution in the passage?

   _____

Read the paragraph and answer the questions that follow.

> Supunnee missed her friends in Thailand, and she wouldn't be going home again for several months. She wondered what her friends were doing, and she felt sad. Then she remembered the friendly girl, Caroline, whom she'd met in class. She decided to give her a call. They made plans to meet before class for lunch. Supunnee felt much better.

3. What is the problem in the passage?

   _____

4. What is the solution in the passage?

   _____

5. How might the skill of identifying problems and solutions help you when reading a story or informational text?

   _____

Name _____ Date _____

Comprehension *Use with Student Edition page 88.*

Choose the best answer for each item. Circle the letter of the correct answer.

1. Yu-Lan dreaded going to school because _____.

   a. she was the smallest student
   b. she was afraid of not understanding people
   c. her mother's bad English embarrassed her

2. Yu-Lan's mother worked in a Chinese-speaking restaurant because _____.

   a. she wanted to cook Chinese food
   b. she wanted to work during the night instead of the day
   c. she didn't know much English

3. When Yu-Lan was upset, her mother _____.

   a. became very quiet
   b. gave her confidence
   c. did not understand

4. Yu-Lan and her mother practiced English by _____.

   a. reading together
   b. going to classes together
   c. speaking English at the restaurant

5. "Quilt" is about the way families _____.

   a. seem brand-new and well put-together
   b. fall apart after many years
   c. stay together even in hard times

Response to Literature *Use with Student Edition page 89.*

In the poem "Quilt," Janet Wong compares the connections between her family members to the threads and fabric in a quilt. The quilt is a symbol of the love in her family. Think about your own family and friends. Write a short paragraph about a symbol that best represents the connections between you and the people you love.

_____
_____
_____
_____
_____

Unit 2 • Reading 2

Grammar Gerunds as Subjects and Subject Complements

Use with Student Edition page 90.

> **REMEMBER** A **gerund** is the *-ing* form of a verb that can function as a noun. When a gerund or gerund phrase is the subject of a sentence, it is followed by a third-person-singular verb. When a gerund is a subject complement, it follows a linking verb, such as *be*. To form a negative gerund, use *not* before the gerund.
> **Example:** *Memorizing the words* is helpful, but my mistake is *not being thorough*.

Complete the sentences with the gerund form of the verbs from the box.

| not drink | surprise | see | bake | wash | walk |

Example: ____Surprising____ someone on his or her birthday is fun.

1. _____ enough water when it's hot is a bad idea.

2. A good form of exercise is _____.

3. _____ a live performance is always exciting.

4. The best way to spend a rainy day is _____ cookies.

5. His least favorite chore at home is _____ the dishes.

Write sentences about yourself with gerunds as subjects or subject complements, using the verbs in parentheses.

Example: (drive) ____Driving long distances makes me sleepy.____

6. (win) _____

7. (travel) _____

8. (give) _____

Name _____ Date _____

Grammar — Gerunds as Objects *Use with Student Edition page 91.*

REMEMBER A gerund or gerund phrase can be the object of certain verbs, such as *appreciate, start, mention,* or *mind*. A gerund or gerund phrase can also be the object of a preposition or certain verb-preposition combinations, such as *participate in, talk about,* and *insist on.*

Complete the sentences with the gerund form of the verbs from the box.

| explain | say | go | eat | meet | run | stand | change |

Example: You should keep _____*going*_____ until you see a stop sign.

1. He has a habit of _____ funny things.
2. The teacher did not bother _____ the answers.
3. I tried _____ on one leg for ten minutes.
4. He began _____ in races when he was fifteen.
5. Did you stop _____ meat?
6. Sammy avoided _____ Jane after their date.
7. I'm considering _____ my major from biology to English.

Write sentences about yourself with gerunds as objects, using the verbs in parentheses.

Example: (cook) _I love cooking a big pot of soup on cold days._

8. (write)
   _____

9. (research)
   _____

10. (bike)
    _____

Unit 2 • Reading 2   47

Writing — **Rewrite a Familiar Story** *Use with Student Edition pages 92–93.*

Complete your own T-chart comparing different characters' points of view from a story you know well.

Have your partner complete (√) the Peer Review Checklist. Use this feedback to help you edit your final draft.

Peer Review Checklist

☐ Does the paragraph help the reader to understand the character's point of view?

☐ Does the paragraph describe the feelings and opinions of the character?

☐ Is the character interesting? Is it well developed?

☐ Are pronouns used correctly?

☐ Are gerunds used as subjects, subject complements, and objects?

☐ What changes could be made to improve the paragraph?

Name _____ Date _____

UNIT 2: What are the benefits of facing challenges?

Reading 3: "A Dark Day with Bright Spots" / "Do This, Not That!"

Vocabulary — Literary Words *Use with Student Edition page 95.*

REMEMBER A **conflict** is a struggle involving a character and outside forces. The way a character responds to conflicts reveals something about that character's **point of view**. A character's point of view drives the conflict in a story and its resolution.

Read each sentence. Write *yes* if it depicts a conflict. Write *no* if it does not depict a conflict.

Conflict?	Description
no	Tom wanted a cup of coffee very badly.
1.	Paolo struggled to cross the stream without falling.
2.	She didn't think she could get past the mean guard dog.
3.	I woke up angry today.
4.	Agi's father always tells her what to do.
5.	The rain made us all wet and cold.

Read the brief author interview below. Circle words and phrases that indicate how the author's point of view affects his writing.

Q: Have your experiences affected your writing at all?

A: Yes, I moved to Chicago from rural Ohio when I was twenty. The move was difficult for me, but I came to love the city. My favorite setting for my stories is Chicago, and my characters often struggle with the hardships of city life. It is easy to meet people in the city, and I had many good friends who helped me. Often my characters will find someone who similarly helps them. The lessons I have learned from people I admire are more important to me than writing about favorite places or things.

Unit 2 • Reading 3

Vocabulary — **Academic Words** *Use with Student Edition page 96.*

Read the paragraph below. Pay attention to the underlined Academic Words.

> The rivers of the northwestern United States are home to millions of salmon. Salmon need to travel up and down the rivers to survive. Unfortunately, many of these rivers are blocked by dams. A map can display where dams are located. Each dam creates lakes and helps make fresh water available to humans. However, the dams also block the salmon's path and have injured or killed many salmon as they try to pass through them.

Write the Academic Words from the paragraph above next to their correct definitions.

Example: ___available___: able to be used or seen

1. _____: continue to live after an accident or illness

2. _____: hurt

3. _____: a setup in a store or other location to show things easily

Use the Academic Words from the paragraph above to complete the sentences.

4. We were surprised that no one was _____ in the crash.

5. I'm not _____ to talk during lunchtime.

6. If you were lost in the woods, would it be possible to _____ on water and berries?

7. Turn right at the giant art _____ in the middle of town.

Complete the sentences with your own ideas.

Example: I want to survive to the age of ___250___.

8. The _____ is a famous display in our town.

9. In our school library, _____ are available as resources to help students learn.

10. If you're not careful, you can get injured while _____.

Name _____ Date _____

Word Study — Closed Compound Nouns

Use with Student Edition page 97.

> **REMEMBER** A **compound noun** is made up of two or more nouns. Compound nouns can be written in different ways. A closed compound noun is written as one word, as in *sailboat*.

Look at the nouns in the boxes below. Then combine the nouns in each row to make a closed compound noun.

Noun	+ Noun	= Compound Noun
stock	broker	*stockbroker*
1. sales	person	
2. data	base	
3. tooth	paste	
4. black	board	
5. sea	port	

Create closed compound nouns by combining the nouns in the box. Then use each closed compound noun in a sentence. Note that nouns may be used more than once.

| burn | bed | coat | room | beam | drop | rain | fall | sun | dial |

Example: _bed + room = bedroom   We painted the bedroom white._

6. _____

7. _____

8. _____

9. _____

10. _____

Unit 2 • Reading 3

Reading Strategy | **Predict** *Use with Student Edition page 97.*

> **REMEMBER** Before you read, predict what a story will be about. You can also make new predictions as you read. Stop from time to time and ask, "What will happen next?" Look for clues in the story. Think about what you already know.

Read the paragraph and answer the questions that follow.

Seeing Stefan Again

One Saturday morning, Angela and her two cousins were riding the subway downtown to the New York Public Library to do research. Two stops before they were going to get off, Angela saw Stefan waiting on a subway platform. She shouted "Stefan!" just before the subway doors closed. He turned just in time to see her before the train left the stop. When they reached the public library stop, Angela got off the train and stood on the platform, stunned she had seen him in the city. She was still standing there when the next train arrived and Stefan stepped through the sliding doors.

---

1. Read the title. What do you predict the story will be about?

   _____

2. Where does the story happen?

   _____

3. When does the story happen?

   _____

4. After you read the paragraph, what do you predict will happen next?

   _____

5. Set a purpose for reading this text.

   _____

Name _____ Date _____

Comprehension Use with Student Edition page 106.

Choose the *best* answer for each item. Circle the letter of the correct answer.

1. Avni's mother was _____, so Avni had to go shopping with her aunt.

   a. busy b. sick c. away on business

2. Auntie Tara wanted Avni to choose clothes that were _____ than Avni preferred.

   a. duller b. brighter c. more formal

3. Before falling to the ground, Auntie Tara thought she saw _____.

   a. spots and shapes b. more clothing than was on the racks c. people talking to Avni

4. To get help for Auntie Tara, Avni _____.

   a. waved to people passing by b. yelled until someone came c. threw clothing in front of the security camera

5. The experience between Auntie Tara and Avni _____.

   a. made Auntie Tara upset b. made them fight with each other more c. drew them closer together

Response to Literature Use with Student Edition page 107.

As you write your incident report, draw a scene that shows a store clerk or security guard coming to help Auntie Tara and Avni. Add what you include in your drawing into your incident report.

Unit 2 • Reading 3

Grammar Passive: Simple Past;
Regular and Irregular Past Participles *Use with Student Edition page 108.*

> **REMEMBER** Use the **passive form** when the focus is on the receiver, not the performer, of an action. A *by*-phrase identifies the performer.
> **Example**: The election was won by the best candidate.
> Create the passive form with the verb *be* + the past participle. Regular past participles are formed by adding *-d* or *-ed* to the base form of the verb. Irregular past participles must be memorized.
> **Example**: The cookies were eaten at the end of the club meeting.

Complete each sentence with the passive form of the verb in parentheses.

Example: (impress) The scientists __were impressed__ by Finlay's theory.

1. (know) Yellow fever _____ as yellow jack.

2. (kill) Troops _____ by the deadly virus.

3. (study) Mosquitoes _____ by Dr. Carlos Finlay.

4. (train) Dr. Walter Reed _____ in the study of bacteria.

5. (find) No cure for yellow fever _____ .

Rewrite each sentence using the passive form.

Example: Ships carried the immature mosquitoes from Africa to America.
 __The immature mosquitoes were carried by ships from Africa to America.__

6. Doctors and scientists read accounts of yellow fever.
 _____

7. Yellow fever claimed millions of lives.
 _____

8. Yellow fever struck the Mississippi Valley.
 _____

9. The researchers proved the doctor's theory.
 _____

10. Vaccines controlled yellow fever.
 _____

Name _____ Date _____

Grammar — Passive Forms of the Verb: Review

Use with Student Edition page 109.

> **REMEMBER** The passive form can be used with any form of a verb. Create the passive with a form of *be* + the past participle. The *be* verb in a passive sentence reflects the form of the verb in the active sentence. For example, in the present perfect (*have* or *has* + past participle), the form of *be* in the passive is *has* or *have* + the past participle of *be* (*been*).
> If there is an object pronoun in an active sentence (*her*), it will change to a subject pronoun in passive (*she*). The word order of the rest of the sentence in the passive form does not change. For example, prepositional phrases that come at the beginning or end of an active sentence remain there in passive.
> **Example:** (active) Someone has pulled the car *out of the ditch*.
> (passive) The car has been pulled *out of the ditch*.

Write the tense of each sentence. Then rewrite each sentence using the passive form. Use the *by*-phrase only when necessary.

Example: The young horse has eaten all the oats. _____present perfect_____
  All the oats have been eaten by the young horse.

1. Someone has designed a new hybrid car. _____

2. The gorilla crushed the tin can. _____

3. Mr. Smith will give a test to our class. _____

4. A person is giving a lecture on the planets at the community center. _____

5. A new teacher is going to teach biology. _____

6. Someone approached me from behind. _____

Unit 2 • Reading 3

Writing: Write a Personal Narrative

Use with Student Edition pages 110–111.

Complete a three-column chart for a personal narrative about a memorable experience you had with a friend or classmate.

Who was there	What happened	What was said

Have your partner complete (√) the Peer Review Checklist. Use this feedback to help you edit your final draft.

Peer Review Checklist

- ☐ Does the paragraph describe a memorable event?
- ☐ Does the paragraph establish a time and place for the setting?
- ☐ Does the writer include dialogue to make the characters seem real?
- ☐ Did the story sustain my interest?
- ☐ Is the passive form used correctly?
- ☐ Are regular and irregular past participles used correctly?
- ☐ What changes could be made to improve the paragraph?

Name _____ Date _____

Writing Workshop *Use with Student Edition pages 116–119.*

Organize your ideas in the graphic organizer below to help create a fictional narrative.

Characters	Setting	Problem	Solution

Have your partner complete (√) the Peer Review Checklist. Use this feedback to help you edit your final draft.

Peer Review Checklist
- ☐ Did the story sustain my interest?
- ☐ Is the plot engaging?
- ☐ Is the action well paced?
- ☐ Is the setting specific and believable?
- ☐ Are the characters interesting? Are they well developed?
- ☐ What changes could be made to improve the story?

Learning Log *Use after completing Student Edition page 120.*

Underline the vocabulary items you know and can use well. Review and practice any you haven't underlined. Underline them when you know them well.

Literary Words	Key Words	Academic Words	
characters conflict point of view	accurate continuous data depth determine theory	accompanied aid challenge code approach communicate	resources response available display injured survive

Put a check by the skills you can perform well. Review and practice any you haven't checked off. Check them off when you can perform them well.

Skills	I can . . .
Word Study	☐ spell words using *ch* and *tch*. ☐ recognize and use prefixes *im-, over-, un-, after-*. ☐ recognize and use closed compound nouns.
Reading Strategies	☐ recognize cause and effect. ☐ identify problems and solutions. ☐ predict.
Grammar	☐ use simple and compound sentences. ☐ use gerunds as subjects, subject complements, and objects. ☐ use the passive form.
Writing	☐ write a story with a starter. ☐ rewrite a familiar story. ☐ write a personal narrative. ☐ write a fictional narrative.

Test Preparation

Test 1

DIRECTIONS
Look at the illustrations and answer the questions.

1 Where is the sign found?

    A In a car
    B In a store
    C By the road
    D By the door

2 A square is a quadrilateral. It is a rhombus because it has four congruent _____. It is a rectangle because it has four 90° angles. All squares are rectangles and rhombi, but all rhombi and rectangles are not squares.

    A geometry
    B similar
    C sides
    D shapes

Test Preparation

Test 2

DIRECTIONS
Read this selection. Then answer the questions that follow it.

Rosa Parks

1. One evening in December 1955, an African-American woman named Rosa Parks left work and boarded a bus in Montgomery, Alabama. She walked toward the back of the bus and sat down in the front row of the section of the bus where African Americans were forced to sit. The bus became crowded and the bus driver told Rosa Parks to give her seat to a white passenger. But Rosa Parks refused and was arrested by the police.

2 Rosa Parks was well-known in the civil rights movement. The following night, Dr. Martin Luther King, Jr. met with other leaders who were fighting for equal rights for African Americans. They decided to protest Rosa Parks' arrest by leading a <u>boycott</u> of public buses in Montgomery. For over a year, most African Americans refused to ride the city's buses.

3 The Montgomery Bus Boycott led to other protests against segregation all over the South. In 1956 the judges of the U.S. Supreme Court ruled that African Americans could no longer be separated from white Americans on public buses. This helped end segregation.

1 What is paragraph 1 mainly about?
  A Why African Americans had to sit at the back of the bus
  B Why Rosa Parks was arrested
  C Why African Americans boycotted buses
  D Why Rosa Parks was well known

2 The selection is best described as —
  A informative
  B humorous
  C persuasive
  D expressive

3 What does the word *boycott* most likely mean?
  A To refuse to use a product or service
  B To fight for equal rights
  C To make a change
  D To force someone to do something

4 According to the selection, the arrest of Rosa Parks —
  A caught the attention of the Supreme Court
  B started protests that helped end segregation
  C happened when she was going to work
  D began the fight for equal rights

Test 3

DIRECTIONS
Read this selection. Then answer the questions that follow it.

Avalanche Survivor

1. One winter day, 17-year-old J.D. Smith and four of his close friends went snowboarding on a remote mountainside outside of Denver, Colorado. They knew it was a risky area but couldn't resist the idea of snowboarding down the untouched, powdery snow.

2. Suddenly the group looked up to see an avalanche starting on the ridge above them. They tried to run but had not taken five steps before the snow was on top of them.

3. "I've never seen anything like it. It looked like pure white coming at us," Smith said later. "It sounded like an earthquake. Just by instinct, I knew that I had to get my hands up to my face, to make an air pocket. Then I just had to ride that snow all the way down and hope for the best."

4. The avalanche carried the boys about a quarter mile down the mountain. Smith was buried under three and a half feet of snow, but it was powdery, so he was able to dig himself out. He started searching for his friends, breaking off a tree branch to probe the snow. He didn't see the next avalanche coming. "It happened really fast," he recalled, "and it was over before I even knew it."

5. The second avalanche carried Smith all the way down to the bottom of the mountain. He was buried just 10 inches below the surface, but the snow was wet and packed, and he couldn't dig himself out. Eventually, he was able to get his head out of the hard snow and call for help. Smith had been trapped for more than an hour when someone nearby heard his calls and helped dig him out. Only one of Smith's friends also survived the powerful avalanches.

1 Look at the timeline.

Timeline of the Avalanches

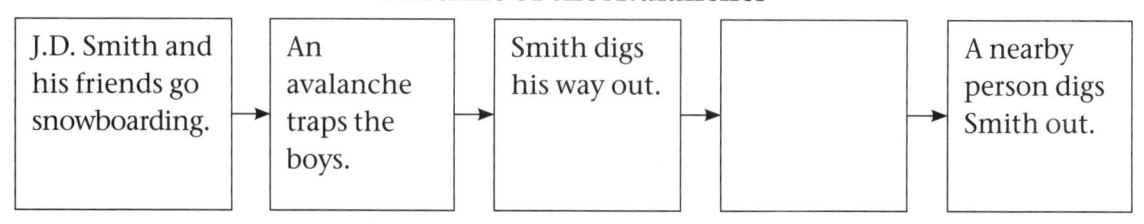

| J.D. Smith and his friends go snowboarding. | → | An avalanche traps the boys. | → | Smith digs his way out. | → | | → | A nearby person digs Smith out. |

Which event BEST completes the timeline of events in the story?

- **A** Smith makes an air pocket with his hands.
- **B** An avalanche carried the boys down the mountain.
- **C** Smith probed the snow.
- **D** A second avalanche hits Smith.

2 Paragraph 4 is mainly about —
- **A** what happened after the first avalanche hit Smith
- **B** what the first avalanche looked like
- **C** what happened when the second avalanche hit the boys
- **D** what the second avalanche sounded like

3 Which of these is the BEST summary of the selection?
- **A** Smith and his friends go to a risky area to snowboard. Smith is buried. He digs out and looks for his friends. A nearby person helps him.
- **B** Smith and his friends go to a risky area to snowboard. An avalanche hits the boys. Another avalanche hits Smith. Smith is buried. He digs out and looks for his friends. A nearby person helps him.
- **C** Smith and his friends go to a risky area to snowboard. An avalanche hits the boys. Smith is buried. He digs out and looks for his friends. A second avalanche hits Smith and buries him. Smith digs out enough to call for help. A nearby person helps him.
- **D** An avalanche hits the boys. Smith is buried. He digs out and looks for his friends. A second avalanche hits Smith and buries him. Smith digs out enough to call for help. A nearby person helps him.

4 According to the article, why did the boys go snowboarding in a risky area?
- **A** They did not think an avalanche could happen.
- **B** They did not know the area was risky.
- **C** They could not resist snowboarding on new snow.
- **D** They thought they could go faster than an avalanche.

(continued)

Name _____   Date _____

Visual Literacy: Smithsonian American
Art Museum *Use with Student Edition pages 122–123.*

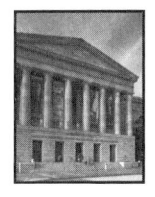

Learning to Look

Look at *The Sick Child* by J. Bond Francisco on page 123 in your Student Edition. Study the hands of the boy and the woman sitting beside him. Write three details about the boy's hands and the clown that he holds. State facts, not opinions.

Boy's Hands

Example: He holds the clown by the leg.

1. _____
2. _____
3. _____

Write three details about the woman's hands and the knitting needles she's working with.

Woman's Hands

4. _____
5. _____
6. _____

Interpretation

Look at *The Sick Child* again. What might the woman be thinking? Write your answers below.

Example: If only his fever would break, he would get well quickly!

_____
_____
_____
_____
_____

Unit 2 • Visual Literacy: Smithsonian American Art Museum

KWLH

Look at *Embroidered Garment* by Alice Eugenia Ligon on page 122 in your Student Edition. Use the artwork to complete the KWLH chart below.

K	W	L	H
What do you **know** about this work of art?	What do you **want** to learn about how the artist made it?	What have you **learned** about the artist and her work?	**How** did you learn this?
		She is a woman.	

Unit 2 • Visual Literacy: Smithsonian American Art Museum

Name _____ Date _____

UNIT 3: How are relationships with others important?

Reading 1: from *Salsa Stories* "Aguinaldo"

Vocabulary — Literary Words *Use with Student Edition page 127.*

REMEMBER **Irony** is the difference between what happens and what a reader expects to happen in a story. Situations of irony can cause surprise and amusement. **Foreshadowing** is an author's use of clues to hint at what might happen later in a story. It builds suspense and shapes the reader's expectations.

Read the description of each situation. Write *irony* if it is an example of irony. Write *foreshadowing* if it is an example of foreshadowing.

Irony or foreshadowing?	Situation
foreshadowing	It was an unusually icy day when they began their car trip. The roads were slippery.
1.	Jeffrey drove for four straight days – only to end up back where he started.
2.	The policeman watched the customer with interest. Then he picked up his radio and said, "Chief, could you check on something for me?"
3.	Our team did well that day. But there were a lot of games left, and things didn't go well for very long . . .

Read the passage. Underline the elements of foreshadowing in the story.

> Miles threw his shoes and shirt into the closet carelessly. He looked down at his desk. There was an unopened letter sitting there, but he tried not to look at it. He opened the window, then shut it again for no reason. The clock seemed to tick more loudly than before. He looked at the picture of his family hanging on the wall. *What if it's bad news?* he thought. He went downstairs for a glass of water, but once he got to the kitchen he forgot to pour it. He thought of his brother, and how much time had passed since his previous letter. Why would he write now? A moment passed. "OK then," Miles said. He marched upstairs, ready for anything. Even bad news.

4. What do you think happens next? _____.

Vocabulary — Academic Words *Use with Student Edition page 128.*

Read the paragraph below. Pay attention to the underlined Academic Words.

> There is a non-profit organization in our town that <u>distributes</u> free lunches to the elderly. Volunteers bring the lunches to elderly <u>residents'</u> homes every day at noon. No elderly person who requests a free lunch is ever turned down, although some feel <u>reluctant</u> to ask for help. Both volunteers and the elderly find delivering and receiving free lunches a very <u>positive</u> experience.

Write the letter of the correct definition next to each word.

Example: __b__ reluctant   a. gives something to different people or places

_____ 1. residents   b. feeling uncomfortable about doing something

_____ 2. distributes   c. good or useful

_____ 3. positive   d. people who live in a place

Use the Academic Words from the exercise above to complete the sentences.

4. Even though the situation was unpleasant, she tried to keep a _____ attitude.

5. All the _____ of the apartment building helped to keep the grounds clean.

6. He was _____ to clear the table just in case people were not done eating.

7. Every Sunday, she _____ flyers to her neighbors to advertise her crafts store.

Complete the sentences with your own ideas.

Example: I had a very positive experience while <u>volunteering at the soup kitchen</u>.

8. If I ask a friend to see a movie with me, I am reluctant to
_____.

9. I like the residents of my neighborhood because _____.

10. Before each class, my teacher distributes _____.

Name _____ Date _____

Word Study — Spelling s- Blends *Use with Student Edition page 129.*

REMEMBER A **consonant blend** is two or three consonants that are placed together in a word. You can hear the sound of each consonant in a consonant blend.

Look at the words in the word box. Underline the consonant blend that begins each word. Then write each word in the correct category in the chart.

| sport | stall | strength | swing | spell | stand | strange | swell | spend | store |

sw-	sp-	st-	str-
swing			

Complete each sentence by adding the correct *s-* blend in the space provided.

1. I want to _____ end more time at home.

2. My favorite _____ ort is soccer.

3. I have to stay in bed so that I can recover my _____ ength.

4. I do not know how to _____ ell that word.

5. It was a very _____ ange movie.

6. I have a _____ omachache.

7. My parents always make me feel _____ ecial.

8. I am going to the _____ ore to buy milk.

Unit 3 • Reading 1

67

Reading Strategy: Recognize Cultural Context

Use with Student Edition page 129.

REMEMBER Analyzing the cultural context of a story helps you visualize and understand what's happening. Notice the author's descriptions and think about the characters' language, country, ideas, and beliefs. Also, think of what you know from your own experiences.

Read the paragraph and answer the questions that follow.

I didn't know what to expect when David invited me to his Chanukah party. He explained that Chanukah is the Jewish festival of lights. We played a game with a four-sided top called a dreidel to win the most Chanukah gelt—foil-wrapped chocolate candy. Later, he and his family lit a special candleholder called a menorah. We had delicious potato pancakes called latkes and later we had special Chanukah doughnuts called sufganiyot. Yum!

1. What culture does the narrator experience?

   _____

2. What does the narrator learn about the culture of the family he or she visits?

   _____

   _____

3. How does the family in this passage feel about their culture?

   _____

   _____

4. Did you learn anything new about Chanukah from this passage?

   _____

   _____

5. How do you think the strategy of recognizing a story's cultural context can help you read with better comprehension?

   _____

   _____

Name _____ Date _____

Comprehension
Use with Student Edition page 138.

Choose the best answer for each item. Circle the letter of the correct answer.

1. Marilia doesn't want to go on the trip to the nursing home because _____.

   a. she is sick
   b. her grandmother died in one
   c. nursing homes are boring

2. An *aguinaldo* is a _____.

   a. nursing home patient
   b. sweet coconut
   c. surprise Christmas gift

3. The morning of the trip, Marilia _____.

   a. is excited
   b. refuses to leave home
   c. pretends to be sick

4. During her time with Elenita, Marilia feels _____.

   a. happy
   b. angry
   c. bored

5. The main irony of the story is that Marilia _____.

   a. spoke to an elderly woman
   b. tried to escape her obligations but couldn't
   c. received an *aguinaldo* of her own

Response to Literature
Use with Student Edition page 139.

By the end of the story, Marilia has made a new friend. If the story continues, and Marilia visits the nursing home again, what do you think will happen?

_____
_____
_____
_____
_____

Unit 3 • Reading 1

Grammar — Imperatives *Use with Student Edition page 140.*

REMEMBER **Imperatives** are often used to give a command or instructions. Form an imperative with the simple present, omitting the subject *you*. To make an imperative negative, add *do not* or *don't* before the verb.
Examples: *Turn on* the oven. *Don't touch* it! It's hot!
Use *please* before an imperative to make a request or offer. Use *let's* before an imperative to include yourself in a suggestion.
Examples: *Please come* with me. *Let's go* together.

Underline all the imperatives and circle all the negative imperatives in the recipe.

<u>Preheat</u> oven to 360 degrees. Mix butter, eggs, and sugar until foamy. Slowly add flour to butter-egg-sugar mixture. In a separate bowl, stir cocoa into a third of the dough. Don't use all the cocoa. Now it is time to pour the dough into the baking pan, alternating layers of light and dark dough. Use a fork to create a pattern. Place the baking pan into the preheated oven.

Rewrite each sentence using an imperative.

Example: You need to use two pieces of bread.
Use two pieces of bread.

1. First you need to use a knife to put peanut butter on both slices.

2. Then you should spread the jelly evenly on both slices of bread.

3. After that, you need to put one slice of bread on top of the other.

4. Next it is time to cut the sandwich in half diagonally.

5. Now you can enjoy your sandwich.

Name _____ Date _____

Embedded Questions *Use with Student Edition page 141.*

> **REMEMBER** An **embedded question** is a type of noun clause and can be the subject or object of a sentence. Embedded information questions begin with a question word, such as *what* or *when*. Embedded *yes / no* questions begin with *if* or *whether*. Use normal word order (subject + verb) for embedded questions. The noun clause is often preceded by phrases such as *I don't know . . . , I wonder . . . ,* and *Could you tell me . . . ?*

Complete each sentence with an embedded question, using the question in parentheses.

Example: <u>How he finished early</u> I'll never know. (How did he finish early?)

1. I wonder _____. (What time does the bus come?)

2. Do you know _____? (Where did Sarah go last night?)

3. I can't remember _____. (What is your address?)

4. _____ is on everybody's mind. (Who will come to the party?)

Correct the errors in the embedded questions in the following sentences.

Example: Do you know what time is it? <u>Do you know what time it is?</u>

5. I don't know where did she go. _____

6. I wonder what does he do. _____

7. Can you tell me who is she? _____

8. I'm not sure when does class begin. _____

Unit 3 • Reading 1

Writing — Write Instructions *Use with Student Edition pages 142–143.*

Complete your own sequence chart containing instructions for something you know how to do well.

First

↓

Then

↓

Next

↓

Finally

Have your partner complete (✓) the Peer Review Checklist. Use this feedback to help you edit your final draft.

Peer Review Checklist

- ☐ Does the first sentence introduce the main idea?
- ☐ Are the instructions clear and easy to follow?
- ☐ Are the instructions given in the correct order?
- ☐ Does the writer use transition words to make the sequence clear?
- ☐ Are imperatives and embedded questions used correctly?
- ☐ What changes could be made to improve the paragraph?

Name _____ Date _____

UNIT 3: How are relationships with others important?

Reading 2: "Inspiring Peace"

Vocabulary — Key Words *Use with Student Edition page 145.*

Write each word in the box next to its definition.

| barriers | confront | cultivate | enemy | political | violence |

Example: ___enemy___ : people who hate you or want to harm you

1. _____ : relating to the government of a country

2. _____ : try to develop a friendship with someone who can help you

3. _____ : things that prevent people from doing something

4. _____ : address someone or something

5. _____ : behavior that is intended to hurt other people physically

Use the words in the box at the top of the page to complete the sentences.

6. The government wants to keep its _____ from getting too strong.

7. It's good to _____ friendships with people who share your interests.

8. Their _____ differences led to an argument about government.

9. He had to _____ the difficult situation.

10. _____ is not the way to solve a problem, because we should try to solve things peacefully.

Unit 3 • Reading 2

Vocabulary — Academic Words *Use with Student Edition page 146.*

Read the paragraph below. Pay attention to the underlined Academic Words.

> When I first met Sanaya, I <u>assumed</u> we could never be friends. She wore very strange clothes and her hair was dyed pink. But I remembered what my mother always said: "Don't judge a book by its cover." One shouldn't just <u>focus</u> on appearance. We are all <u>individuals</u> and each person has value. So I decided that if I just tried talking to Sanaya, maybe I would like her. I was right! We discovered we had many <u>similarities</u>. Now she is my best friend.

Write the Academic Words from the paragraph above next to their correct definitions.

Example: ___focus___ : pay special attention to a particular person or thing instead of others

1. _____ : the qualities of being similar, or the same

2. _____ : thought that something was true without having proof

3. _____ : people; not a whole group

Use the Academic Words from the paragraph above to complete the sentences.

4. The students preferred to receive their diplomas one at a time, as _____.

5. The student _____ he had done well on the test, but he was wrong.

6. The girls learned that their _____ were as important as their differences.

7. This week in history class we will _____ on the War of the Roses.

Complete the sentences with your own ideas.

Example: Two similarities between my friend and me are _our tempers and our interest in history_.

8. After school I like to focus on _____.

9. For a long time, I assumed that _____.

10. I think that it's important for people to be treated as individuals because _____.

74   Unit 3 • Reading 2

Name _____ Date _____

Word Study   Suffixes *-er*, *-or*   Use with Student Edition page 147.

REMEMBER A **suffix** is a letter or group of letters placed at the end of a base word. Adding a suffix changes the meaning of the base word. Adding the suffix *-er* or *-or* to a base word adds the meaning "one who." **Example:** *Traveler* means "one who travels."

Look at the base words and suffixes in the chart. Add the suffix *-er* or *-or* to create a new word. Then write the definition of the word using the verbs in the box.

| teach | sing | play | facilitate | create | visit | act | read | write | own |

Base Word	+ Suffix	= New Word	Definition
write	-er	writer	one who writes
1. instruct	-or		
2. perform	-er		
3. inspect	-or		
4. believe	-er		
5. create	-or		
6. review	-er		
7. edit	-or		
8. direct	-or		

Complete each sentence by adding *-er* or *-or* in the space provided. Use a dictionary if needed.

9. The act_____ was great in his role as a spy.

10. Diego is the best play_____ on our soccer team.

11. The artist was a brilliant sculpt_____.

12. My mother is the own _____ of a business.

13. We have a visit _____ at our school today.

14. Mr. Jones is my favorite teach_____.

15. I'd like to be a photograph_____.

Unit 3 • Reading 2

Reading Strategy | **Compare and Contrast**

Use with Student Edition page 147.

> **REMEMBER** When you compare, you see how things are similar. When you contrast, you see how things are different. Comparing and contrasting can help you understand what you read.

Read each paragraph. Then answer the questions that follow.

Dara and Dora are identical twins. They look the same with dark hair and big brown eyes. Their friends call them opposites, however. Dara is smart but grumpy. Dora is pleasant but lazy.

1. How are Dara and Dora alike?

   _____

   _____

2. How are Dara and Dora different?

   _____

   _____

The United Kingdom and the United States have a lot in common. English is the first language in both countries. Both countries have been the most powerful nations in the world. However, the United Kingdom is small and the United States is large. In the U.K., people love soccer, rugby, and cricket; in the U.S. they favor American football, basketball, and baseball—although football is becoming more popular than ever.

3. How are the United States and the United Kingdom alike?

   _____

   _____

4. What are some differences between the United Kingdom and the United States?

   _____

   _____

5. How can comparing and contrasting make you a better reader?

   _____

   _____

Name _____ Date _____

Comprehension   Use with Student Edition page 152.

Choose the *best* answer for each item. Circle the letter of the correct answer.

1. The purpose of Seeds of Peace is to _____.

   a. teach people how to argue about politics and religion
   b. help bring understanding to the Middle East
   c. perform research on kids

2. Seeds of Peace combines regular camp activities with _____.

   a. two-hour dialogue sessions
   b. international competitions
   c. history lessons about Palestine and Israel

3. Professional facilitators help campers to discuss _____.

   a. why people live in different regions
   b. which religion is better and more ancient
   c. their own experiences and difficulties

4. The campers at Seeds of Peace hope to _____.

   a. become leaders in their own communities
   b. become camp counselors
   c. no longer communicate with people from neighboring regions

5. Sometimes the conversations among the campers can get heated because they _____.

   a. disagree about the camp
   b. come from feuding regions
   c. do not get along with the facilitator

Extension   Use with Student Edition page 153.

Look up areas of the world where conflict and war are ongoing. Who is involved in each conflict? How long has it gone on? Write the results of your research in the chart.

Location	Who is involved?	How long?
Afghanistan	Afghanistan, the Taliban, the United States	since 2001

Unit 3 • Reading 2

Grammar — Complex Sentences *Use with Student Edition page 154.*

REMEMBER A **complex sentence** consists of a main clause and at least one subordinate clause joined with a subordinating conjunction. A main clause has a subject and a verb and expresses a complete thought. A subordinate clause has a subject and a verb, but does NOT express a complete thought. When a complex sentence begins with a subordinate clause, a comma follows the clause.

Underline the subordinate clause(s) and circle the main clause in each sentence.

Example: (When Noor joined the camp,) he didn't know that he would meet Shirlee.

1. At the camp, Arabs and Israelis meet for the first time and they learn to get along.
2. Sometimes the campers fight with each other because they disagree.
3. Although the Arab and Israeli students disagree on many topics, before Seeds of Peace, they disagreed even more.
4. Until people from warring regions get along, there will always be problems.
5. Before Seeds of Peace, many children would not have been friends.

Join the clauses with the subordinating conjunction in parentheses.

6. (because) The camp was amazing. I learned a lot about the world.
   _____

7. (before) The situation got out of control. The counselors would help us talk about the issues.
   _____

8. (although) Many of our discussions were heated. We never got angry at each other.
   _____

9. (because) I made new friends. There were so many interesting people.
   _____

10. (after) I told my friends about Seeds of Peace. They wanted to join.
    _____

Name _____ Date _____

Agreement in Complex Sentences *Use with Student Edition page 155.*

> **REMEMBER** The main and subordinate clauses in a complex sentence should be in agreement. When a clause is in the present and has a singular subject, be sure to use a singular verb. Also, pronouns must agree with their antecedents. In the example, both clauses are in the present. The singular subject, *Allie*, agrees with the verb *wants*; the singular subject *she* agrees with *needs*. The pronoun *she* agrees with its antecedent, *Allie*, and the pronoun *them* agrees with its antecedent, *Paul and David*.
> **Example:** If *Allie wants* to drive with *Paul and David*, *she needs* to call *them* right away.

Correct the errors in verb form in the following sentences.

Example: Every mother ~~love~~ *loves* her child because she ~~had~~ *has* an instinct to.

1. When John slipped and fell, he were running down the stairs.

2. I doesn't know where I was going. Can you help me?

3. While we was eating dinner, the phone rings.

4. Until spring come, we isn't planting our garden.

Complete each sentence with the correct pronoun(s) that agrees with the underlined antecedent.

Example: Although <u>the cat</u> was fat, <u>it</u> was very active.

5. <u>The children</u> stayed in _____ rooms because _____ were being punished.

6. Although <u>John</u> forgot _____ lines during rehearsal, _____ remembered them during the performance.

7. <u>The boy</u> ate _____ snack after _____ finished his homework.

8. <u>Children</u> sometimes have toys that _____ carry with _____ until _____ start school.

Unit 3 • Reading 2

79

Writing — Write a Critique *Use with Student Edition pages 156–157.*

Complete your own content web with ideas for a critique of a story, movie, video game, or place you have visited.

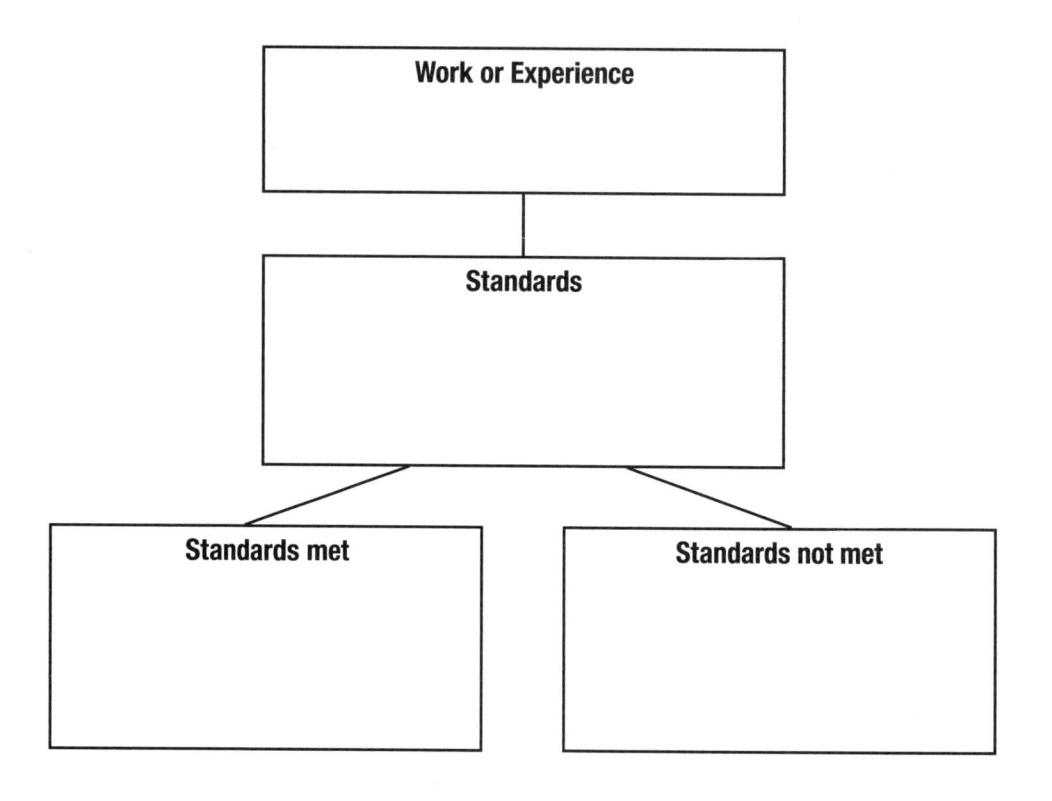

```
        ┌─────────────────────────┐
        │   Work or Experience    │
        └─────────────────────────┘
                     │
        ┌─────────────────────────┐
        │       Standards         │
        └─────────────────────────┘
               /           \
   ┌──────────────────┐   ┌──────────────────┐
   │  Standards met   │   │ Standards not met│
   └──────────────────┘   └──────────────────┘
```

Have your partner complete (√) the Peer Review Checklist. Use this feedback to help you edit your final draft.

Peer Review Checklist

☐ Does the first sentence introduce the topic?
☐ Does the paragraph clearly identify the criteria for evaluation?
☐ Does the writer evaluate the event or experience according to the criteria?
☐ Is the writer's opinion clear?
☐ Are connecting words used to link ideas and create complex sentences?
☐ Do nouns and pronouns agree in complex sentences?
☐ What changes could be made to improve the paragraph?

Name _____ Date _____

UNIT 3: How are relationships with others important?

Reading 3: from *Blue Willow*

Vocabulary — Literary Words Use with Student Edition page 159.

REMEMBER **Oral tradition** is the practice of storytellers passing stories down from one generation to the next. These stories sometimes included a **legend**, or traditional story that moves away from factual events to describe more fictional events and characters. **Character motivation** is a reason that explains a character's thoughts, feelings, action, and speech.

For each situation listed, give the motivation of the main character.

Motivation	Situation
fatigue	Luke put down the ax and wiped his brow. Almost done, he thought, and then I can finally go to sleep!
1.	"I don't want to see it," Deng said. He backed away from the display slowly, shaking. "It's too awful to even think about," he added.
2.	DeWayne looked greedily at the stack of $20 bills that would be given out as prizes. He grinned and rubbed his hands. "I'd like to enter the contest," he said.
3.	Corrina looked at the clock every few minutes. When the day was over, her parents would arrive. If she could have made time move faster by working harder, she would have.

Does one of the passages have the characteristics of a legend? Write *yes* or *no*.

4. _____ Thor raised his hammer and struck the earth to scare away the fiery dragon. Behind the dragon he could see treasure boxes spilling over with gold.

5. _____ The weather in Miami, Florida, is often humid and hot. Even in the winter, the temperatures can be in the high 70s and low 80s.

Unit 3 • Reading 3

Vocabulary — Academic Words *Use with Student Edition page 160.*

Read the paragraph below. Pay attention to the underlined Academic Words.

> John's uncle is an <u>authoritative</u> figure among the Dagomba people of northern Ghana. He is a griot—someone who tells stories through music. John had always wanted to visit him. Last month, after getting the <u>consent</u> of his uncle, John's parents surprised him with a plane ticket to Ghana. His <u>reaction</u> was pure excitement. John spent two weeks in Ghana and his uncle taught him how to play a "talking drum." John's <u>encounter</u> with his uncle was one he will never forget.

Write the letter of the correct definition next to each word.

Example: __c__ reaction

____ 1. authoritative

____ 2. encounter

____ 3. consent

a. respected and trusted as being true, or making people respect or obey you

b. an occasion when you meet someone without planning to

c. the way you behave in response to someone or something

d. permission to do something

Use the Academic Words from the exercise above to complete the sentences.

4. The forest ranger had an unexpected _____ with a grizzly bear.

5. The students all had a positive _____ to the field-trip announcement.

6. Before the operation could begin, the patient had to give her _____.

7. This article contains several mistakes, so it is not an _____ source.

Complete the sentences with your own ideas.

Example: __The Senator__ is an authoritative leader.

8. When I get bad news, my reaction can range from _____ to _____.

9. I need parental consent before I can _____.

10. I once had a funny encounter with _____.

Name _____ Date _____

Word Study — Synonyms *Use with Student Edition page 161.*

REMEMBER Synonyms are words that have the same or nearly the same meaning.
Example: *loud* and *noisy*

For each word in column 1, find its synonym in column 2. Write the letter of the synonym next to each word.

1. pretty _____
2. kind _____
3. mean _____
4. large _____
5. expensive _____

a. costly
b. cruel
c. nice
d. attractive
e. big

For each of the words below, write a synonym. Use a thesaurus or dictionary if needed.

6. ask _____
7. inform _____
8. knowledge _____
9. shout _____
10. detest _____
11. beautiful _____
12. small _____
13. clever _____
14. unusual _____
15. cheap _____

Unit 3 • Reading 3   83

Reading Strategy: Identify with a Character

Use with Student Edition page 161.

REMEMBER When you identify with a character, you try to understand the actions and feelings of a character. This can help you enjoy and understand a story.

Read each paragraph. Then answer the questions that follow.

Martina saw that Grayson had left his social studies test right on the library table. Nobody else was around. If she wanted to, she could take a quick look at his answers. After all, Grayson was the most brilliant student in the class. Martina hadn't taken the test herself. But on the other hand, what would Grandma Rose think if she found out that her granddaughter was a cheater? I need a good grade! she thought. *What should I do?*

1. What choice is Martina facing in this passage?

   _____

2. What would you do if you were Martina, and why?

   _____

   _____

Zach loved creating music. He played guitar, drums, and piano, and recorded his songs on his computer. He knew they were getting better all the time. However, he had a problem: when he opened his mouth to sing, he was always off-key. Then he learned about the band contest. The winner could get a scholarship to music school. It was everything he dreamed about. How could he show how good his music was when he couldn't sing?

3. What does the main character care about in this passage?

   _____

4. What problem does Zach face in this passage?

   _____

5. How can the strategy of identifying with a character help you become a better reader?

   _____

   _____

Name _____ Date _____

Comprehension Use with Student Edition page 170.

Choose the best answer for each item. Circle the letter of the correct answer.

1. Kung Shi Fair and Chang the Good _____.

   a. never meet in the story
   b. are sworn enemies
   c. fall in love

2. The merchant attempts to _____.

   a. keep Kung Shi Fair and Chang the Good apart
   b. scare the villagers with stories about a ferocious leopard
   c. bring people together

3. Kung Shi Fair and Chang believe that _____.

   a. they will kill the leopard
   b. one day they will marry
   c. the merchant will bring them gifts

4. The merchant insists that Kung Shi Fair wait for _____.

   a. two swallows
   b. a rainbow
   c. a bolt of lightning

5. If the merchant had not been so stubborn, then perhaps _____.

   a. his daughter would have lived
   b. he would have caught the leopard
   c. Chang might never have met Kung Shi Fair

Response to Literature Use with Student Edition page 171.

Write a different ending to the story *Blue Willow*. Tell what might have happened if Kung Shi Fair's father had approved of the poor fisherman.

_____
_____
_____
_____
_____

Grammar

Transitions *Use with Student Edition page 172.*

REMEMBER The transitions and transitional phrases *however*, *on the other hand*, and *instead* contrast two ideas. *As a result*, *therefore*, *thus*, and *consequently* show cause-and-effect. Use a period when a transition or transitional phrase connects two sentences; use a semicolon when connecting two independent clauses. A comma follows a transition or transitional phrase when it begins a sentence or clause. Commas offset a transitional phrase midsentence, but a comma is not used with most one-word transitions midsentence. One exception is *consequently*, which is offset with commas.

Circle all the correct transitions to complete each sentence.

Example: Jerome volunteered for the Peace Corps. (However /(As a result)/(Therefore)), he went into relief work.

1. She didn't like the blue dress. (Thus / Instead / However), she liked the green one.
2. The principal awarded Roger honors. Roger, (as a result / on the other hand / consequently), went to the best university.
3. Marcia ate too much cake; (consequently / instead / thus), she had a stomachache.
4. I'm not fond of fish. (Instead / Therefore / On the other hand), I love shellfish.

Add punctuation (commas, semicolons, and periods) to correct the use of the transitions in the sentences below.

5. Becky studies a lot therefore she gets good grades.
6. Adam doesn't like to play video games instead he enjoys reading.
7. We practiced every day for weeks Consequently the concert was a success.
8. Chuck was hungry after running As a result he ate six eggs.

Name _____ Date _____

Grammar — Adjectives *Use with Student Edition page 173.*

REMEMBER Adjectives describe nouns and can be placed in different categories based on their qualities. Use a chart like the one shown to order adjectives that describe the same noun.

Determiner	Opinion	Size	Age	Shape	Color	Material	Origin	Purpose	NOUN
odd-looking	ugly	big	old	thin	black	metal	used	exercise	bike

Complete each sentence by placing the adjectives in the correct order.

Example: We bought a <u>small</u>, <u>round</u> cake for her birthday.

1. That _____, _____ bird just flew off the branch. (red / tiny)

2. We looked on the map at the _____, _____, _____ route to the city. (winding / long / rural)

3. There are no more _____, _____, _____ desserts left in the kitchen. (delicious / chocolate / heart-shaped)

4. My best friend has _____, _____, _____ hair. (curly / red / long)

Complete the sentences with your own ideas.

Example: I can see the <u>long</u>, <u>winding</u> stream from the hilltop.

5. I would describe soccer as a(n) _____, _____ sport.

6. Our school is having a(n) _____, _____ bake sale.

7. As part of the performance, there was a(n) _____, _____, _____ chorus.

8. We saw a(n) _____, _____, _____ giraffe at the zoo.

Unit 3 • Reading 3

Writing: Write to Compare and Contrast

Use with Student Edition pages 174–175.

Complete your own Venn diagram comparing and contrasting two people, places, or things you know well.

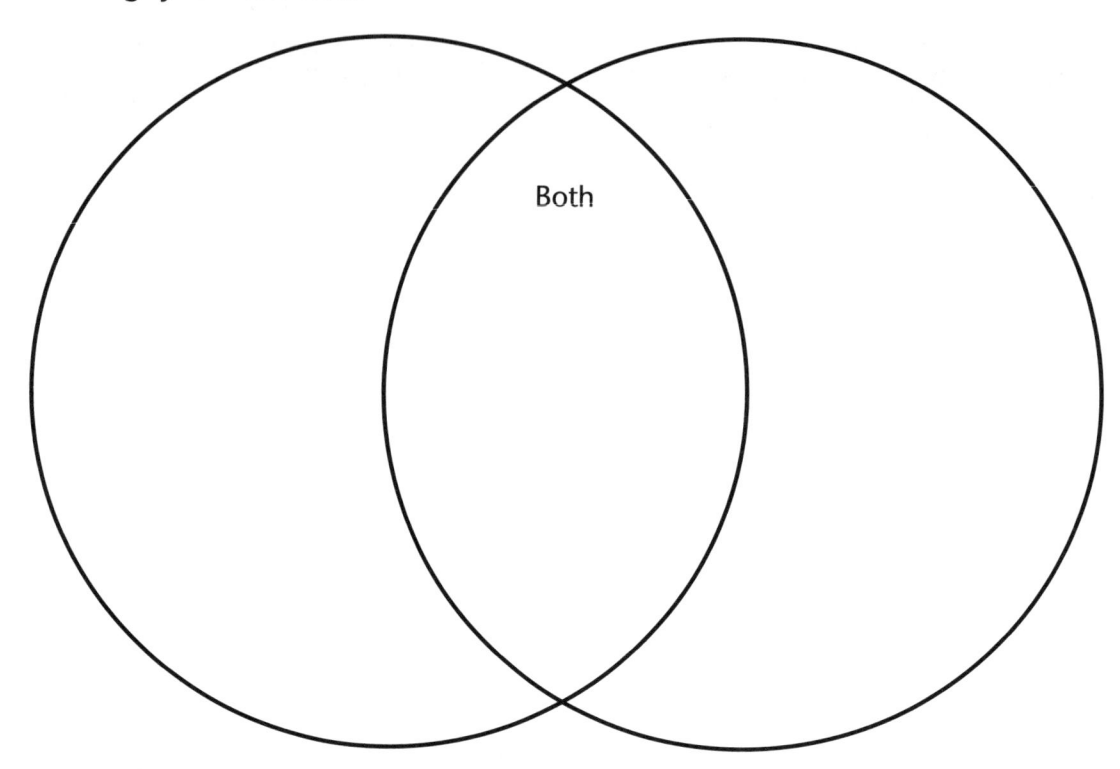

Both

Have your partner complete (✓) the Peer Review Checklist. Use this feedback to help you edit your final draft.

Peer Review Checklist

- ☐ Does the first sentence explain what is being compared or contrasted?
- ☐ Does the paragraph describe similarities and differences?
- ☐ Does the paragraph include specific examples to support the main points?
- ☐ Are compare and contrast structures used correctly?
- ☐ Are transitions used to contrast ideas?
- ☐ Are adjectives ordered correctly?
- ☐ What changes could be made to improve the paragraph?

Name _____ Date _____

Writing Workshop   *Use with Student Edition pages 180–183.*

Organize your ideas in the graphic organizer below to help draft an expository essay.

Have your partner complete (√) the Peer Review Checklist. Use this feedback to help you edit your final draft.

Peer Review Checklist
- ☐ Was the essay clearly organized?
- ☐ Was the information interesting?
- ☐ Did I understand the topic better after reading it?
- ☐ Did the first paragraph introduce the topic?
- ☐ Did the concluding paragraph sum up the main points?
- ☐ What changes could be made to improve the essay?

Learning Log *Use after completing Student Edition page 184.*

Underline the vocabulary items you know and can use well. Review and practice any you haven't underlined. Underline them when you know them well.

Literary Words	Key Words	Academic Words	
foreshadowing irony oral tradition legend character motivation	barriers confront cultivate enemy political violence	distributes positive reluctant residents assumed focus	individuals similarities authoritative consent encounter reaction

Put a check by the skills you can perform well. Review and practice any you haven't checked off. Check them off when you can perform them well.

Skills	I can . . .
Word Study	☐ spell words using *-s* blends. ☐ recognize and use the suffixes *-er* and *-or*. ☐ recognize and use synonyms.
Reading Strategies	☐ recognize cultural context. ☐ compare and contrast. ☐ identify with a character.
Grammar	☐ use imperatives and embedded questions. ☐ use complex sentences. ☐ use agreement in complex sentences. ☐ use transitions. ☐ use adjectives.
Writing	☐ write instructions. ☐ write a critique. ☐ write to compare and contrast. ☐ write an expository essay.

Name _____ Date _____

Test Preparation

Test 1

DIRECTIONS
Read this selection. Then answer the questions that follow it.

The Red River War

1   In the mid-1800s, the United States <u>expanded</u> west. Native Americans living on land that belonged to the United States were forced to leave their homes. The tribes were moved to reservations. The reservations were not like the homes the Native Americans left behind. The government gave them food. They trained to be farmers. But this was not the life that many of the Native Americans wanted.

2   In 1874, some of the Native Americans were not on reservations. A few attacked a group of buffalo hunters in Texas. The army then declared war on all Native Americans who were not on reservations. Leaders of the tribes were sent to Florida. The Native Americans did not have leaders on the reservations. Soldiers hunted any Native American in the area. Native Americans were forced onto the reservations or killed.

3   In 1875, the army negotiated with the last group of Native Americans outside of the reservations. Their leader, Quanah Parker, led his people to Fort Sill, ending the war.

  1 What is the purpose of the selection?
    A To inform the reader about an important event
    B To persuade the reader to visit Fort Sill
    C To explain to the reader how to live in peace
    D To describe to the reader life on the reservations

  2 In the selection, what does <u>expanded</u> mean?
    A lived
    B hunted
    C spread
    D traveled

Test Preparation

Test 2

DIRECTIONS
Read this selection. Then answer the questions that follow it.

The Bald Eagle

1. The bald eagle is the national bird of the United States. This beautiful bird is the only eagle that is unique to North America. It is also one of the largest North American birds. Adult male eagles have a wingspan of about six and a half feet. The female eagles are even larger. They have a wingspan of about eight feet. They can fly at speeds of thirty miles per hour.

2. Eagles eat fish, other birds, and small mammals. They spot their prey from the air because they can see it from several hundred feet away. Then they dive to catch their food. They can dive as fast as 100 miles per hour. They grab their prey in their talons and fly away. They can lift prey that weighs about five pounds.

3. Eagles live for thirty years or more. Eagles also live in pairs and have the same partner for life. A pair of eagles builds a large nest in a big tree near a river or lake. Because the eagles add new material to their nest each year, a single nest may weigh up to 2,000 pounds.

1. What is paragraph 2 mainly about?
   A The wingspan of bald eagles
   B How bald eagles find and catch food
   C Bald eagle nests
   D Where to find bald eagles

2. According to the article, where do bald eagles build their nests?
   A On cliffs
   B In small trees
   C In trees near the ocean
   D In big trees

3. In paragraph 2, what words help the reader know what *prey* means?
   A they spot
   B from the air
   C eat fish
   D mile away

4. The author probably wrote this article to —
   A persuade people to protect bald eagles
   B give information about bald eagles
   C explain how bald eagles became the national symbol
   D give an opinion about bald eagles

Name _____ Date _____

Test 3

DIRECTIONS
Read this selection. Then answer the questions that follow it.

Shirley and Jenny

1   Shirley, like many elephants transported overseas, has had a hard life. Shirley was born in the jungle of Indonesia in 1948. Five years later, she was captured and sold to a circus in the United States. She performed under the circus big top for more than twenty years. Then in 1975, when Shirley was twenty-eight, another elephant attacked her and broke one of her back legs. Her leg was not treated properly, and Shirley's recovery took many months. She could hardly walk. Shirley was sold to a zoo in Louisiana. It was a small zoo, and Shirley was the only elephant. She lived there for twenty-two years and had no contact with other elephants. In 1999, the zoo gave Shirley, now fifty-one, to the Elephant Sanctuary, a new 120-acre <u>sanctuary</u> in Tennessee. The Elephant Sanctuary is a place where people take care of neglected elephants.

2   On her first day at the sanctuary, Shirley did not want to go outside. A younger elephant named Jenny entered the stall next to Shirley's. Through the bars separating the stalls, Jenny and Shirley touched trunks. Immediately Jenny and Shirley became very excited and started to roar. When the sanctuary staff opened the gate between the stalls, Shirley and Jenny comforted each other for a long time. Then Jenny led Shirley out into the green pastures of the sanctuary. From that moment, the two elephants were always together.

3   The staff at the Elephant Sanctuary searched the records and discovered that Shirley and Jenny had worked together in the circus when Jenny first arrived in the United States. They had been together for only a few months, but during that time they became attached to each other. Perhaps Shirley had been like a mother to the five-year-old Jenny. After more than twenty years apart, they were finally together again.

Test Preparation

1 Look at the timeline below.

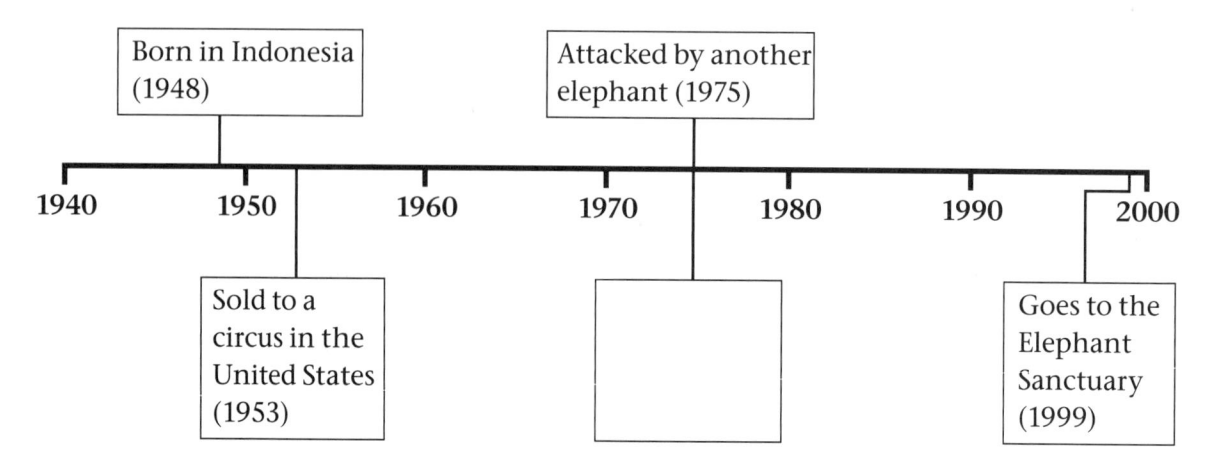

```
Born in Indonesia          Attacked by another
(1948)                     elephant (1975)

1940    1950    1960    1970    1980    1990    2000
         |                                        |
      Sold to a                              Goes to the
      circus in the                          Elephant
      United States                          Sanctuary
      (1953)                                 (1999)
```

Which of the following belongs in the box?

A Performed under the big top
B Sold to a zoo in Louisiana
C Transported to the United States
D Meets Jenny

2 Paragraph 2 is mainly about —

A Shirley's life in the circus
B Shirley's reluctance to go outside
C the reunion of Shirley and Jenny
D the sanctuary staff

3 In paragraph 1, what words help the reader know what sanctuary means?

A a place
B in Tennessee
C take care
D 120-acre

4 The reader can conclude that Shirley —

A will miss performing in the circus
B will continue to be happy at the sanctuary
C will become upset at the sanctuary
D will miss Jenny

5 Which sentence in paragraph 2 shows that Shirley was happy to see Jenny?

A A younger elephant named Jenny entered the stall next to Shirley's.
B Immediately Jenny and Shirley became very excited and started to roar.
C Through the bars separating the stalls, Jenny and Shirley touched trunks.
D Then Jenny led Shirley out into the green pastures of the sanctuary.

Name _____ Date _____

Visual Literacy: Smithsonian American Art Museum *Use with Student Edition pages 186–187.*

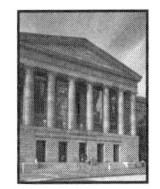

Learning to Look

Look at *Placa/Rollcall* by Charles "Chaz" Bojórquez on page 187 in your Student Edition. The artist uses shapes in place of letters in this painting. Find the shapes and then list as many as you can. State facts, not opinions.

Example: _____triangle_____

1. _____   4. _____
2. _____   5. _____
3. _____   6. _____

Interpretation

Look at *Merce C* by Franz Kline on page 186 in your Student Edition. Imagine that each of the brushstrokes in the painting is a dancer. Describe his or her movements.

Example: The brushstroke on the right looks like it is moving an arm.

_____
_____
_____
_____
_____
_____

What sounds or music is the dancer dancing to? Explain your answer.

_____
_____

5W&H

Look at *Placa/Rollcall* by Charles "Chaz" Bojórquez again. If you could interview Chaz's friends, whose names appear in his artwork, what would you ask them? Use questions that begin with *Who, Where, When, What, Why,* and *How*.

Example: Where __did you grow up?__

7. Who _____

8. Where _____

9. When _____

10. What _____

11. Why _____

12. How _____

Name _____ Date _____

UNIT 4 — What does home mean?

Reading 1: "97 Orchard Street" / "The Pros and Cons of Tenement Life"

Vocabulary | **Key Words** *Use with Student Edition page 191.*

Write each Key Word in the box next to its definition.

| exhibit | inspector | mission | ~~neighborhood~~ | preserved | tenement |

Example: _neighborhood_ : a small area of town

1. _____ : an assignment or purpose
2. _____ : apartment house in a poor area of a city
3. _____ : something shown to the public
4. _____ : kept from harm or change
5. _____ : official who examines things carefully

Use the words in the box at the top of the page to complete the sentences.

6. The museum's _____ is to tell the story of the old town.
7. We visited an art gallery where a new _____ was on display.
8. The _____ looked around and said the wiring was safe.
9. The residents of the _____ were proud of their new library.
10. The family from China _____ many old Chinese traditions.

Unit 4 • Reading 1   97

Vocabulary   **Academic Words** *Use with Student Edition page 192.*

Read the paragraph below. Pay attention to the underlined Academic Words.

> Heirlooms are <u>items</u> that are passed down from one family member to another. One <u>benefit</u> of keeping this tradition alive is that heirlooms give children of <u>immigrants</u> an <u>incentive</u> to learn more about their ancestors' country. The design of the heirloom usually tells something about the <u>cultural</u> background it came from. For example, people in an Irish <u>community</u> sometimes wear a ring called a *Claddagh*. The ring is usually passed down from parents to their children. The ring shows two hands holding a heart, with a crown on top. These are symbols of ancient Ireland.

Write the letter of the correct definition next to each Academic Word.

Example: __b__ cultural

_____ 1. immigrants   a. people who enter another country in order to live there

_____ 2. benefit   b. relating to a particular society and its way of life

_____ 3. community   c. all the people living in one place

_____ 4. incentive   d. something that encourages or motivates

                 e. something that helps you or gives you an advantage

Use the Academic Words from the exercise above to complete the sentences.

5. The _____ were happy in their adopted country.

6. The annual parade brought together people in the _____.

7. One _____ of a balanced diet is more energy.

8. Traveling in a foreign country is a(n) _____ to learn some of the language.

Complete the sentences with your own ideas.

Example: Most of the immigrants in my community are from ___Haiti___.

9. An incentive for me to learn English is _____.

10. One benefit of living in a diverse community is _____.

Name _____ Date _____

Word Study — Silent Letters *Use with Student Edition page 193.*

REMEMBER The letters *gn*, *bt*, *mb*, and *kn* stand for one sound, not two. For example: the *g* is silent in *gnome*, the *b* is silent in *indebted*, the *b* is silent in *plumber*, and the *k* is silent in *knead*. Knowing when letters are silent will help you spell and pronounce words correctly.

Read the words in the box below. Then write each word in the correct column in the chart.

| designing | knowledge | crumb | gnarled | knack | undoubted |
| plumber | doubt | doubted | knob | thumb | gnaw |

Words with *gn*	Words with *bt*	Words with *mb*	Words with *kn*
designing			

Identify and write the silent letter in each word below.

Example: knoll _____silent k_____

1. gnat _____
2. assign _____
3. doubtful _____
4. knot _____
5. tomb _____
6. reign _____
7. knitting _____
8. bomb _____
9. knee _____

Unit 4 • Reading 1

Reading Strategy — Use Visuals
Use with Student Edition page 193.

REMEMBER Visuals are the art, photographs, diagrams, charts, and maps that can come with a text. You can use visuals to learn more about the topic.

Look at the pictures and the text and answer the questions that follow.

About 12 million immigrants entered the United States through Ellis Island between 1892 and 1954. Roughly one-half of U.S. citizens have at least one ancestor who passed through here.

First- and second-class passengers did not have to go through Ellis Island. They were inspected aboard ship. If they were healthy and didn't have legal problems, they left when the ship docked. Third-class passengers had to go to Ellis Island to have physical, mental, and legal examinations.

The chart shows that 1907 was Ellis Island's busiest year. The busiest day was April 17, 1907, when 11,747 immigrants arrived. After World War I, the United States opened embassies around the world, where people filled out forms and had medical exams before traveling. In November 1954, the last person left Ellis Island. In September 1990, the main building reopened as a museum. About two million people visit every year.

Year	Number of People Entering Ellis Island
1892	445,987
1898	178,748
1907	1,004,756
1919	26,731
1924	315,587

(Source: Annual Reports of the Commissioner General of Immigration, 1892–1924. Washington, D.C.)

1. What do you think the article is about? _____

2. How does the picture help you understand the text?

3. How does the chart help you understand the text? _____

4. What is one interesting thing you learned from the information given? _____

5. How do you think the skill of using visuals can help you understand the text?

Comprehension — *Use with Student Edition page 198.*

Choose the best answer for each item. Circle the letter of the correct answer.

1. The museum at 97 Orchard Street in New York City allows visitors to _____.

   a. meet people who grew up at that address
   b. see the immigrant experience firsthand
   c. do the same work that immigrants did in factories

2. The museum shares immigrant history by presenting _____.

   a. audio lectures
   b. apartments of immigrants from long ago
   c. movies and books

3. The United States' most famous gateway for immigrants was at _____.

   a. the Lower East Side
   b. the Upper West Side
   c. Staten Island

4. In the early 1900s, new immigrants found social support and assistance in _____.

   a. their home countries
   b. their jobs
   c. fraternal groups

5. Tenement life created many _____.

   a. cultural problems
   b. health problems
   c. financial problems

Extension — *Use with Student Edition page 199.*

Research five groups of immigrants that came to the United States. Find out where they settled in large numbers and what neighborhoods they formed there. Write the groups and the names of their new neighborhoods on the chart below.

Immigrant Group	Neighborhoods (U.S. city)
Italians	Little Italy (NYC), North End (Boston)

Unit 4 • Reading 1

Grammar: Adjectival Clauses: Subject Relative Pronouns

Use with Student Edition page 200.

> **REMEMBER** An adjectival clause beginning with a relative pronoun describes a noun in an independent clause. A nonrestrictive adjectival clause gives extra information and is set off with commas. A restrictive adjectival clause is necessary to understand the antecedent to which it refers and is not set off with commas. When the relative pronoun is the subject of the adjectival clause, use *who* to refer to a person, *that* to refer to a thing in a restrictive clause, and *which* to refer to a thing in a nonrestrictive clause.
> **Example:** My new Prius, *which is parked over there*, was hit by a red car *that fled the scene of the accident*.

Circle the correct relative pronoun in each sentence below.

Examples: People (*who*/which) travel are called tourists.

1. People (who / which) arrive in New York City by ship see the Statue of Liberty.
2. The statue, (that / which) is in Lafayette Park, was made by Berge.
3. The man (who / which) designed the statue was French.
4. Visitors explore the city, (who / which) has dozens of neighborhoods.
5. They travel on trains (who / that) run underground.

Circle the correct subject relative pronoun. Then complete each sentence with your own ideas.

Examples: My mom's stories, (*which*/ that) __are always about our family__, are my favorite.

6. The people (who / which) live in my neighborhood _____.
7. My favorite book, (who / which) sits on my shelf, _____.
8. My best friend, (who / that) lives _____, _____.
9. The immigrants (who / which) came to this country _____
   _____.
10. The homes (who / that) were built a hundred years ago _____
    _____.

Name _____ Date _____

Grammar — Adjectival Clauses: Object Relative Pronouns

Use with Student Edition page 201.

> **REMEMBER** When a relative pronoun is the object of the adjectival clause, use *whom* to refer to people, *that* (in restrictive clauses) and *which* (in nonrestrictive clauses) to refer to things, *where* to refer to places, *when* to refer to times, and *whose* to show possession. Object relative pronouns come at the beginning of the clause. Be sure to use commas with nonrestrictive clauses.
> **Example:** The Darjeeling Café, *where we went for my birthday*, has closed down.

Complete the sentences with *whom, that, which, where, when,* or *whose.*

Example: The woman ____*whom*____ I met at the play called me.

1. We are staying in Astoria, _____ my friend lives.

2. A visitor can take a tour, _____ volunteers give.

3. The tours usually end at 5:00 P.M., _____ the museum closes.

4. The tour guide _____ I saw earlier is leaving.

Write each pair of sentences as one using the correct object relative pronoun.

Example: The salesclerk was very rude. I waited in her line.
   The salesclerk whose line I waited in was very rude.

5. The concert was great. It ended late.
   _____

6. I told you about the movie. I saw it last night.
   _____

7. Denmark is in northern Europe. I've always wanted to go to Denmark.
   _____

8. My only brother is graduating tomorrow. You met him last night.
   _____

Unit 4 • Reading 1

Writing **Write a Magazine Article** *Use with Student Edition pages 202–203.*

Complete your own 5Ws chart for a magazine article about an event in your town.

Who?	
What?	
Where?	
When?	
Why?	

Use the Peer Review Checklist below to obtain feedback from your partner. This feedback will help you edit your final draft.

Peer Review Checklist

- ☐ Does the first sentence introduce the topic?
- ☐ Does the paragraph answer the 5W questions about the topic?
- ☐ Does the writer grab the reader's attention with interesting information?
- ☐ Is the vocabulary appropriate to the topic?
- ☐ Are adjectival clauses used correctly?
- ☐ What changes could be made to improve the article?

Name _____ Date _____

UNIT 4 — What does home mean?

Reading 2: "A Tree Grows in Brooklyn"

Vocabulary — **Literary Words** Use with Student Edition page 205.

> **REMEMBER** Setting is the time and place of a story. Authors provide the reader with details to understand the where and when of the story. Authors may also use a **flashback** to provide the reader with more information. A flashback is something that happened at a time earlier than the main story.

Read each excerpt from a story. Write *yes* if it describes the setting. Write *no* if it does not.

Setting?	
	"What happened here exactly?" the woman asked.
1.	It was a scene of complete devastation. There wasn't a tree standing in the forest.
2.	The man's face was frozen, like he had seen a ghost.
3.	The sun was setting, and a cold wind was starting to blow.

Write one or two sentences describing each setting. Be creative. Use a flashback where appropriate.

Setting	Sentences
an old house	*Every window in the old house was broken and the yard was overgrown with weeds. It had once been the finest home on the boulevard.*
4. a city street	
5. a time in the future	

Unit 4 • Reading 2   105

Vocabulary Academic Words *Use with Student Edition page 206.*

Read the paragraph below. Pay attention to the underlined Academic Words.

> Despite his short height, and guidance from his family to try other sports, Ali could think of nothing other than playing basketball. He was on the court every spare moment he had. Finally, his parents recognized that when determination like their son's occurs, it has to indicate that some things are just meant to be.

Write the Academic Words from the paragraph above next to their correct definitions.

Example: ___occurs___ : happens

1. _____ : advice or recommendation

2. _____ : having a firm purpose

3. _____ : say or do something that shows what you want or intend to do

Use the Academic Words from the paragraph above to complete the sentences.

4. A lunar eclipse, where the moon is in the earth's shadow, _____ twice a year.

5. It was only through her incredible _____ that she was able to succeed.

6. Please _____ that you know the answer by raising your hand.

7. I don't usually take _____ from others well, but in this case I knew he was right.

Complete the sentences with your own ideas.

Example: The best guidance I ever got was *to find work that makes you happy.*

8. A clear sign of determination is _____.

9. Something that occurs every day at my school is _____.

10. I often indicate how I feel by _____.

Name _____ Date _____

Word Study — Homophones Use with Student Edition page 207.

REMEMBER Homophones are words that sound the same but are spelled differently and have different meanings. For example, *I*, *aye*, and *eye* are homophones. *I* means "me"; *aye* means "yes"; and *eye* means "the part of your face that you see with." When you use or read a homophone and are unsure of its meaning and part of speech, look it up in a dictionary.

Write your own definitions for each pair of homophones in the chart. Then check your definitions in a dictionary.

Homophones	Definitions
Example: ad, add	advertisement, to total
1. heir, air	
2. bald, bawled	
3. barren, baron	
4. steel, steal	
5. tease, teas	

Write definitions for each pair of homophones below. Use a dictionary if necessary. Then use both words in sentences that show their meanings. You can write a sentence for each word or use both words in one sentence.

Example: tense, tents nervous; canvas housing structures
The kids feel tense when they are camping in tents and see bears coming!

6. bazaar, bizarre _____

7. threw, through _____

8. sighs, size _____

9. leak, leek _____

Unit 4 • Reading 2   107

Reading Strategy | **Summarize** *Use with Student Edition page 207.*

> **REMEMBER** To summarize, find the main ideas and state them in a few short sentences. Leave out details and focus on the most important points.

Read each passage. Then answer the questions that follow.

There are many ways to travel between the U.S. cities New York and Boston. You can take the fast train, which takes 3 ½ hours. You can take the bus, which takes about 4 hours. You can drive in your own car, which takes about 4 hours. You can take a plane, which takes just 1 hour.

1. Summarize the passage above in one sentence.

    _____

2. Which details did you leave out of your summary?

    _____

Homes come in all kinds of shapes and sizes. Igloos are homes made of ice and snow. Log cabins are homes made of wood. Many homes in cities are tall apartment buildings made of steel and concrete. Whatever type of home a person has, all that really matters is that it feels safe and warm.

3. Summarize the passage above in one sentence.

    _____

4. What details did you leave out of your summary?

    _____

5. How can the strategy of summarizing help you to better understand what you read?

    _____

Comprehension *Use with Student Edition page 214.*

Choose the *best* answer for each item. Circle the letter of the correct answer.

1. Francie liked the smell of her library better than the smell of her _____.

   a. house   **b.** church   **c.** school

2. Francie asked the librarian for guidance choosing a book _____.

   a. once a month   **b.** every day   **c.** once a week

3. Francie liked looking at the pottery jug because it changed with the _____.

   a. seasons   **b.** months   **c.** holidays

4. Francie's favorite setting to read in on Saturdays was _____.

   a. on the branch of a tree   **b.** on the fire-escape   **c.** in the old, shabby library

5. Francie once started copying a book because she _____.

   a. wanted to have her own book   **b.** had to write a report for school   **c.** damaged a library book

Response to Literature *Use with Student Edition page 215.*

Write a short paragraph describing what you think Francie will be like when she's older. What are some careers she might choose?

_____
_____
_____
_____
_____

Unit 4 • Reading 2   **109**

Grammar: Adjectives and Adjectival Phrases

Use with Student Edition page 216.

> **REMEMBER** An adjective or adjectival phrase modifies, or describes, a noun or noun phrase. It usually comes before the noun it describes or after a linking verb. A prepositional phrase can also function as an adjective; if follows the adjective it modifies.

Underline the adjective(s) or adjectival phrase in each sentence. Circle the noun or noun phrase that is modified.

Example: (The woman) from our office is tall and intelligent.

1. We picked wild mushrooms from the forest.
2. A slim, elegant woman entered the room.
3. The movie about the dog was wonderful.
4. John is a young man full of ideas.

Answer each question using the adjectival phrase in parentheses.

Example: How was the movie? (sad but interesting)

It was sad but interesting.

5. What kind of person is he? (nice, thoughtful)

   _____.

6. What kind of dancer is she? (talented and graceful)

   _____.

7. How was the movie? (boring, without much plot)

   _____.

8. What kind of cheese is this? (goat, from Switzerland)

   _____.

Name _____ Date _____

Adverbs and Adverbial Phrases *Use with Student Edition page 217.*

> **REMEMBER** An adverb or adverbial phrase modifies a verb, an adjective, or another adverb. Many adverbs that modify verbs are formed by adding *-ly* to an adjective.
> A prepositional phrase can also modify a verb, telling place and time.
> **Example:** She doesn't *usually* work *at the hospital on Saturdays*.
> A qualifier is a type of adverb that modifies another adverb or adjective. Adverbs can appear in numerous places in a sentence, but qualifiers like *quite*, *very*, *rather*, etc. appear before the word they modify.
> **Example:** He walked *rather quickly* because he was *very* happy to see me.

Underline the adverb(s) or adverbial phrase(s) in each sentence. Circle the verb, adjective, or adverb that is modified.

Example: The girl <u>patiently</u> (waited) <u>in the car</u>.

1. He politely opened the door.

2. The man walked quickly to the shop.

3. He marched very proudly in the parade.

4. They lived happily in Canada for many years.

Insert the adverb(s) or adverbial phrase(s) correctly into each sentence. More than one answer may be possible.

Example: She danced. (gracefully, in the moonlight)
           gracefully   in the moonlight

5. She reacted to the news. (quite calmly)

6. Joan arrived. (finally, at the cafe)

7. Serena buys stamps. (very often, downtown)

8. A tall man entered the room. (rather, quietly)

Unit 4 • Reading 2   111

Writing — **Write a Plot Summary** *Use with Student Edition pages 218–219.*

Complete your own plot summary chart for a story from a book, film, or television show you know well.

Characters
Setting
Conflict
Main events
Resolution

Use the Peer Review Checklist below to obtain feedback from your partner. This feedback will help you edit your final draft.

Peer Review Checklist

- ☐ Does the paragraph include only the main points?
- ☐ Does the paragraph describe the characters, the setting, and the main events of the story?
- ☐ Does the paragraph explain the main conflict and the resolution of the story?
- ☐ Are adjectives and adverbs included?
- ☐ Are adjectival and adverbial phrases included?
- ☐ What changes could be made to improve the paragraph?

Name _____ Date _____

UNIT 4 — What does home mean?

Reading 3: *The Lotus Seed*

Vocabulary — **Literary Words** Use with Student Edition page 221.

REMEMBER The **speaker** of a poem is the character who tells the poem. A **symbol** is anything that stands for something else. It has its own meaning, but can also stand for an idea or feeling.

Read each sentence. Write whether it contains a symbol or a line of a poem narrated by a speaker.

Sense	Description
speaker	I think you're like a summer day, / Please listen and I'll count the ways
1.	We stand watching / leaves falling in autumn
2.	The statue represented happiness.
3.	Do you remember the smell of evening? / We shared it, smiling

Read the two poems below. Circle the clues that help you determine who the speaker is. Then write who the speaker is. The first clue has been circled.

(When I was ten-and-three)
I'm certain I did see
A tiny brontosaurus
I'm sure it said to me
"I live beneath a certain tree
Right here, deep in the forest."
Dear grandson, this is true!
It might happen to you . . .

4. _____

We float above waiting,
Rumble and light,
High overhead.
Gather and burst
Then tumble and down,
Splatter and splash
We pool at your feet
And race down your rivers
And dampen your hair.
How else would we meet?

5. _____

Unit 4 • Reading 3   113

Vocabulary — Academic Words *Use with Student Edition page 222.*

Read the paragraph below. Pay attention to the underlined Academic Words.

> My grandmother removed the ruby ring she was wearing and showed it to me. She said, "I'm very <u>attached</u> to this ring. It's very <u>significant</u> to me because it was my own grandmother's." I <u>examined</u> the small, but very beautiful, ring. By my grandmother's smile, I could see that the ring was a source of great pleasure for her. "A ruby can <u>symbolize</u> love," she said.

Write the Academic Words from the paragraph above next to their correct definitions.

Example: __examined__ : observed carefully

1. _____ : represent a quality or feeling

2. _____ : emotionally connected to

3. _____ : important

Use the Academic Words from the paragraph above to complete the sentences.

4. On the American flag, the stars _____ the 50 states.

5. Solar energy is a _____ source of power in my country.

6. The puppies were _____ to their mother right away.

7. I _____ the book closely to make sure it was mine.

Complete the sentences with your own ideas.

Example: Children grow very attached to __their pets__.

8. Doves often symbolize _____.

9. The doctor examined _____.

10. A significant part of my diet is _____.

114   Unit 4 • Reading 3

Name _____ Date _____

Word Study — Spelling Long o *Use with Student Edition page 223.*

REMEMBER The long *o* sound can be spelled several different ways. These include *o* as in *cold*, *oa* as in *roast*, *o_e* as in *bone*, and *ow* as in *show*. Knowing these sound-spelling relationships will help you spell and say words with long *o* correctly.

Read the words in the box below. Then write each word in the correct column in the chart.

| ~~pagoda~~ | moan | swallow | zone | toast | snow |
| aglow | loaf | hello | vote | ago | telephone |

Words with long *o* spelled *o*	Words with long *o* spelled *oa*	Words with long *o* spelled *o_e*	Words with long *o* spelled *ow*
pagoda			

For each word below, write the letter or letters that stand for the long *o* sound.

Example: colt ____long o spelled o____

1. boast _____
2. hold _____
3. strove _____
4. row _____
5. float _____
6. unknown _____
7. grown _____
8. nowhere _____
9. tone _____

Unit 4 • Reading 3

Reading Strategy | **Analyze Text Structure**

Use with Student Edition page 223.

> **REMEMBER** When you read, analyze text structure by studying the way the parts of a text are arranged. Remember that poems and plays have a special text structure. They are arranged in lines and groups of lines called stanzas. Narrative poems are written in verse. Punctuation doesn't always follow the same rules in poetry as it does in other types of text.

Read each passage below. Then answer the questions that follow each passage.

Every day
In every way
I try to grow
Strong and proud

1. What is the text structure of the passage above?

   _____

2. Are there rhyming lines in the passage above? If so, what are they?

   _____

   KIM: We have to solve the mystery!
   JUAN: I told you already. It's too dangerous!
   KIM: If we don't solve it, who will?
   JUAN: Promise me that one day you'll stop dragging me into your adventures!
   KIM: Does that mean you'll help me solve the mystery?
   JUAN: I guess I have no choice.

3. What is the text structure of the passage above?

   _____

4. What do the words in bold represent in this text structure?

   _____

5. How can the strategy of analyzing text structure help you become a better reader?

   _____

Comprehension *Use with Student Edition page 228.*

Choose the best answer for each item. Circle the letter of the correct answer.

1. The speaker's grandmother takes the lotus seed in order to _____.

    a. give it to her grandchildren
    b. remember the emperor
    c. remember Vietnam

2. When the grandmother's family left the country, she _____.

    a. took the lotus seed
    b. took her hair combs
    c. took water from the River of Perfume

3. For the grandmother, the lotus seed symbolizes _____.

    a. a new life in the United States
    b. the old ways in Vietnam
    c. the Vietnam War

4. When Bà sees the lotus blossom growing in her garden, she feels _____.

    a. remorse
    b. anger
    c. hope

5. The seed allows the speaker to _____.

    a. connect her life to her grandmother's life in Vietnam
    b. plant her own garden
    c. see the golden dragon throne of the emperor

Response to Literature *Use with Student Edition page 229.*

In *The Lotus Seed*, the seed acts as a symbol for the grandmother. Think of your own family and your heritage. What symbol would you choose to represent your memories and traditions? Write a short paragraph describing this symbol.

_____

_____

_____

_____

_____

Unit 4 • Reading 3

Grammar: Adverbial Clauses of Time
Use with Student Edition page 230.

REMEMBER Adverbial clauses of time are subordinate, or dependent, clauses that express *when* and are used with a main, or independent clause. Adverbial clauses begin with subordinating conjunctions (*after, before, when, while, as soon as, by the time, until, whenever*). Each of these shows a different time order. For example, *as soon as* and *by the time* imply that the action in the adverbial clause must be finished before the second action can happen. *Until* implies an action in the future. *When* is often used with a clause in the simple form; *while* is often used with a clause in the progressive form.

Underline the adverbial clause in each sentence. Circle the subordinating conjunction.

Example: We went out to dinner (when) my father got home.

1. Whenever my aunt visits, we get presents.
2. I plan to be a doctor after I graduate.
3. As soon as you know the answer, raise your hand.
4. You can't go until you finish your homework.
5. The caterpillar will turn into a butterfly by the time it matures.

Complete the sentences with information about yourself.

Example: _I usually read a book_ whenever it rains.

6. When we don't have school, _____.
7. _____ after school lets out for summer.
8. As soon as I save enough money, _____.
9. By the time I'm 25, _____.
10. _____ while I was doing my homework.

Name _____ Date _____

Adverbial Clauses of Purpose, Reason, and Contrast

Use with Student Edition page 231.

> **REMEMBER** An adverbial clause, like other adverbs, can modify the action of a sentence. To express the purpose of an action, use the subordinating conjunctions *in order that* or *so that*. To express the reason for an action, use *because*, *since*, or *as*. To contrast two actions, use *although*, *even though*, or *though*.
> When an adverbial clause begins a sentence, it is followed by a comma.

Underline the adverbial clause in each sentence. Write whether it is an adverbial clause of *purpose, reason,* **or** *contrast.*

Example: He couldn't swim <u>since it was winter</u>. _____reason_____

1. Although he enjoyed his vacation, he was ready to go home. _____

2. Marty built a tree house so that he would have his own private place.
   _____

3. As it was almost noon, the teacher postponed our test. _____

4. In order that we could leave early, my father left work at three. _____

Combine the pairs of sentences with an appropriate subordinating conjunction. More than one answer is possible.

Example: Ariana came home early. She was having a good time.
   Ariana came home early even though she was having a good time.

5. I joined the soccer team. I could get into shape.
   _____

6. Jessica took off her sweater. It was warm inside the house.
   _____

7. He likes sports cars. He likes to drive fast.
   _____

8. School usually begins in September. This year, it began in August.
   _____

Writing   Write a Response to Literature

Use with Student Edition pages 232–233.

Complete your own idea web for a response to a story or another piece of literature.

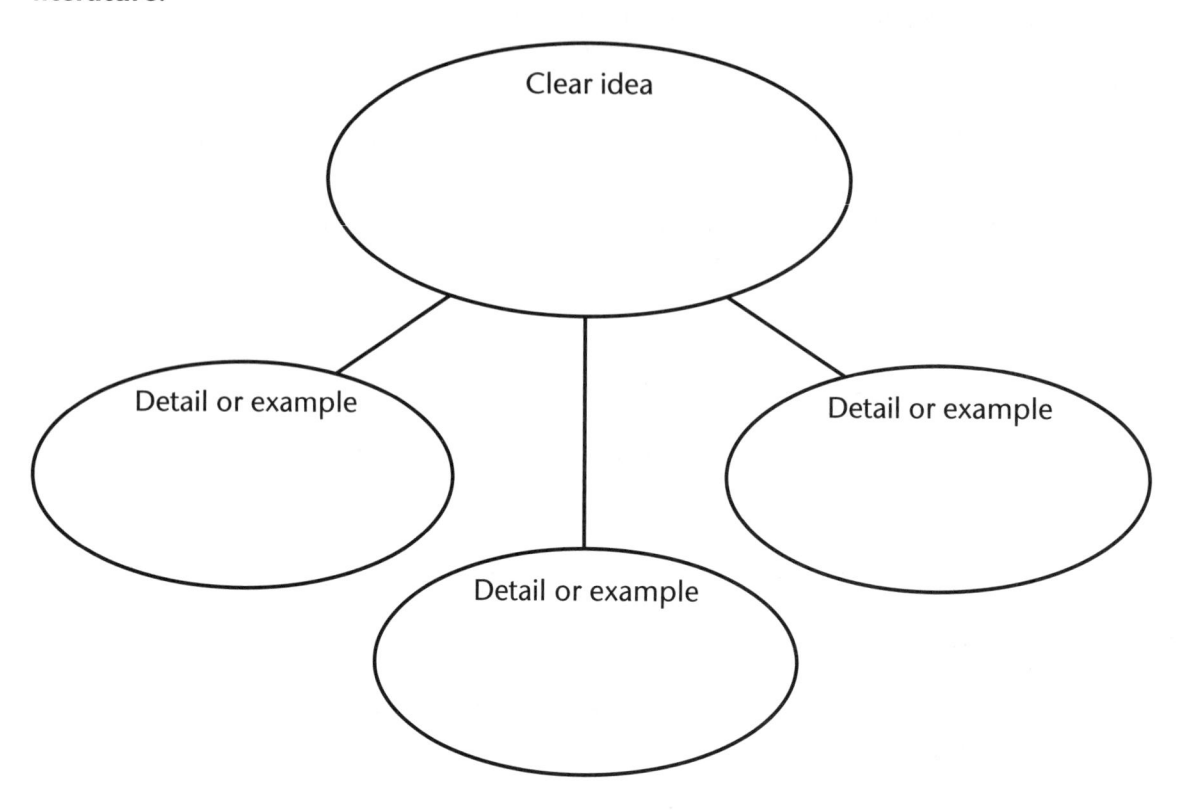

- Clear idea
  - Detail or example
  - Detail or example
  - Detail or example

Use the Peer Review Checklist below to obtain feedback from your partner. This feedback will help you edit your final draft.

Peer Review Checklist

- ☐ Does the paragraph explain the main idea of the story or poem?
- ☐ Does the paragraph explain how the main idea is developed through the details of the story or poem?
- ☐ Are the statements supported with evidence from the text?
- ☐ Is the paragraph clearly organized?
- ☐ Are adverbial clauses of time used correctly?
- ☐ Are adverbial clauses of purpose, reason, and contrast used correctly?
- ☐ What changes could be made to improve the paragraph?

Name _____ Date _____

Writing Workshop *Use with Student Edition pages 238–242.*

Organize your ideas in the graphic organizer below.

> I.
>   A.
>   B.
> II.
>   A.
>   B.
> III.
>   A.
>   B.
> IV.
>   A.
>   B.
> V.
>   A.
>   B.

Use the Peer Review Checklist below to obtain feedback from your partner. This feedback will help you edit your final draft.

Peer Review Checklist
- ☐ Was the essay clearly organized?
- ☐ Was the information interesting?
- ☐ Did I understand the topic better after reading it?
- ☐ Did the first paragraph introduce the topic?
- ☐ Did the concluding paragraph sum up the main points?
- ☐ What changes could be made to improve the essay?

Learning Log Use after completing Student Edition page 242.

Underline the vocabulary items you know and can use well. Review and practice any you haven't underlined. Underline them when you know them well.

Literary Words	Key Words	Academic Words	
flashback setting speaker symbol	exhibit inspector mission neighborhood preserved tenement	benefit community immigrants incentive determination guidance indicate occurs	attached examined significant symbolize

Put a check by the skills you can perform well. Review and practice any you haven't checked off. Check them off when you can perform them well.

Skills	I can . . .
Word Study	☐ spell words with silent letters. ☐ recognize and use homophones. ☐ recognize and spell words with long *o*.
Reading Strategies	☐ use visuals. ☐ summarize. ☐ analyze text structure.
Grammar	☐ use subject and object relative pronouns in adjectival clauses. ☐ use adjectives and adjectival phrases. ☐ use adverbs and adverbial phrases. ☐ use adverbial clauses of time, purpose, reason, and contrast.
Writing	☐ write a magazine article. ☐ write a plot summary. ☐ write a response to a piece of literature.

Name _____ Date _____

Test Preparation

Test 1

DIRECTIONS
Read this selection. Then answer the questions that follow it.

Coming Home

1. Natalia and her family had a terrific vacation. Visiting family in Colombia is always fun. Natalia played with cousins she had not seen in years.

2. The long plane ride home made Natalia tired. Her little sister Anna whined and cried. Mother tried to quiet her. Father gave Anna candy. Nothing worked.

3. Anna curled up against Natalia's shoulder. Natalia talked softly to the girl. She told Anna that she should fall asleep. If she did, she could dream about home. Anna could play with her friends. She could play with her toys. Anna could dream of lying in bed with Natalia in their own bedroom.

4. All the talking made Natalia very sleepy. She <u>drifted off</u>, still holding Anna's hand. She had sweet dreams. Soon she heard Anna calling her name. They were finally home.

1 According to the passage, Natalia visited _____.
   A her parents and sister
   B cousins at the airport
   C family in Colombia
   D friends back home

2 In the selection, what does <u>drifted off</u> mean?
   A floated away
   B landed softly
   C flew away
   D fell asleep

Test Preparation   **123**

Test 2

DIRECTIONS
Read this selection. Then answer the questions that follow it.

Mammals

1   Mammals are animals that produce living young, feed their babies milk, and breathe using lungs. Humans, lions, and bears are examples of mammals. Most mammals make their home on land. For example, lions live in prairies, plains, and savannah grasslands. These large areas of land are covered with grasses and have very few trees or shrubs. Bears live in forests and woods. Some mammals, like whales and dolphins, make their home in water. They can be found in oceans around the world.

2   All mammals have fur or hair to keep them warm and protect their bodies. The amount of hair or fur they have depends on the climate of their home. Mammals that live in cold weather, such as polar bears, usually have a lot of fur or hair to keep them warm. Mammals that live in warmer climates often do not have as much hair because it takes less to keep their bodies warm. Elephants, whales, and humans are examples of mammals that don't have a lot of hair. In fact, whales have hair only on their face.

1 What is paragraph 1 mainly about?
   A Where mammals live
   B Where lions live
   C Where whales live
   D Where bears live

2 How did the author organize this article?
   A The article defines mammals and explains why mammals have fur or hair.
   B The article explains why mammals live on land and water. Then the article describes why mammals have different amounts of hair.
   C The article defines mammals, describes where they live, and explains why mammals have different amounts of hair.
   D The article compares and contrasts different kinds of mammals.

3 In paragraph 2, what word or words help the reader know what *climate* means?
   A fur or hair
   B cold weather
   C their home
   D polar bears

4 Why do elephants have less hair than polar bears?
   A They live in a cold climate.
   B They live on the plains.
   C They do not need to keep warm.
   D They live in a warm climate.

Name _____ Date _____

Test 3

DIRECTIONS
Read this selection. Then answer the questions that follow it.

Taro and the Sea Dragon's Palace

1. Many years ago in a small village by the Sea of Japan, there lived a poor young fisherman named Taro Urashima. One day, Taro noticed some boys teasing a baby sea turtle with sticks and stones. Taro felt sorry for the turtle, so he rescued it and put it back into the ocean.

2. Some time later when Taro was fishing, a giant sea turtle <u>emerged</u> from the water. Taro was startled when he saw the turtle rise up from the ocean. The turtle thanked Taro for rescuing him and offered to take him to the Sea Dragon's Palace at the bottom of the sea so that Princess Oto might thank him, too. Never having seen the bottom of the sea, Taro agreed. He jumped onto the turtle's back, and they went deep into the ocean.

3. Taro and the turtle arrived at an enormous golden palace. The beautiful Princess Oto welcomed Taro inside. She had prepared a great feast with the most delicious food Taro had ever tasted. After dinner, the princess asked if Taro would like to stay at the palace. Taro agreed, and each day thereafter was filled with wonders and riches.

4. After some time, Taro began to feel homesick. The princess wept when he told her this, but Taro was determined to return home. As a parting gift, the princess gave Taro a jeweled box. She told him to always keep it with him but never to open it.

5. When Taro arrived back at his village, he didn't recognize any of the people. When he went to his parents' house, it wasn't there. He asked an old woman where the Urashima family could be found. She laughed and said the Urashima family had been gone for over a hundred years.

6. Sitting by the sea, very sad and confused, Taro looked at the box Princess Oto had given him. Forgetting her warning, he opened it. A huge cloud of green smoke came out. When the smoke cleared, Taro was an old man. He had been at the Sea Dragon's Palace for many, many years.

Test Preparation

1. Which sentence from the selection shows that Taro is kind?
   A *After some time, Taro began to feel homesick.*
   B *He jumped onto the turtle's back, and then went deep into the ocean.*
   C *Taro felt sorry for the turtle, so he rescued it and put it back into the ocean.*
   D *One day, Taro noticed some boys teasing a baby sea turtle with sticks and stones.*

2. Paragraph 5 is mainly about —
   A how the village changed while Taro was in the sea
   B how the village had grown while Taro was in the sea
   C how the old lady reacted to Taro
   D where Taro's family home had gone

3. In paragraph 2, what words help the reader know what *emerged* means?
   A was startled
   B was fishing
   C rise up
   D some time later

4. The reader can conclude that before Taro opened the box —
   A he thought the box would help him find his family
   B he looked the same as the day he went into the sea
   C he wanted to return to the golden palace
   D he wanted to find out where his family had gone

5. In paragraph 2, the phrase "Never having seen the bottom of the sea" tells the reader that Taro —
   A is afraid of the ocean
   B likes to visit new places
   C has not been to the ocean before
   D does not like visiting new places

Name _____ Date _____

Visual Literacy: Smithsonian American Art Museum *Use with Student Edition pages 244–245.*

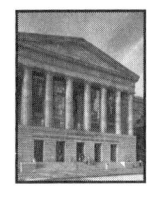

Learning to Look

Look at *Camas para Sueños* by Carmen Lomas Garza on page 244 in your student book. Use that artwork to complete the web diagram below. For each "string" in the diagram, write a detail that you see. State facts, not opinions.

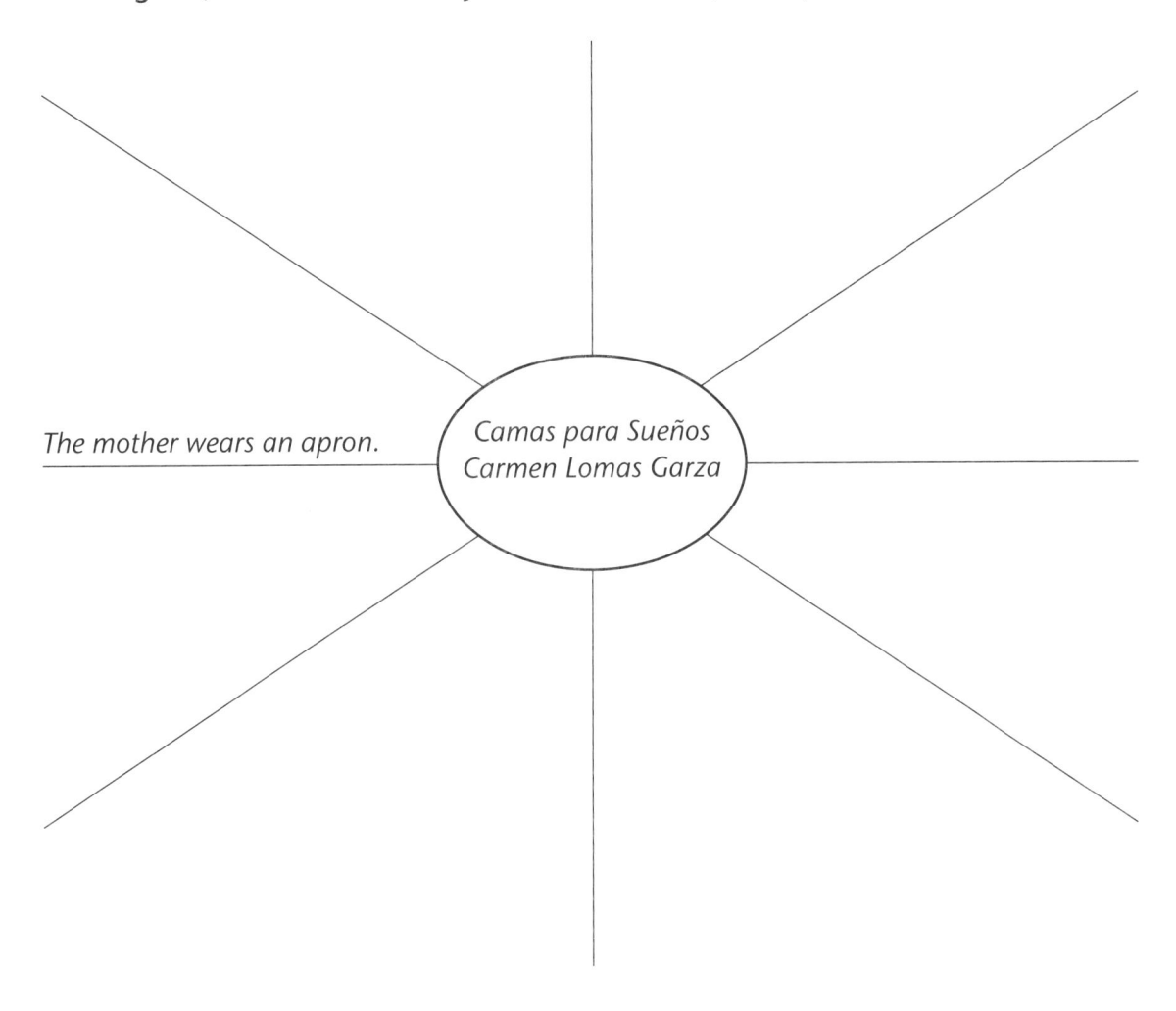

The mother wears an apron.

Camas para Sueños
Carmen Lomas Garza

Interpretation

Look at *The Ocean Is the Dragon's World* by Hung Liu on page 245 of your student book. What title would you give Hung Liu's painting?

Example: <u>I would call this painting <u>The Great Empress</u> because it shows a royal Chinese woman.</u>

Write your title and explain why you chose it.

_____
_____

Compare & Contrast

Look at *The Ocean Is the Dragon's World* and *Camas para Sueños* again. Write three details about the woman in *The Ocean Is the Dragon's World*.

Example: <u>The woman has very long fingernails.</u>

1. _____
2. _____
3. _____

Write three details about the mother in *Camas para Sueños*.

4. _____
5. _____
6. _____

How are the two figures similar?

_____
_____

How are the two figures different?

_____
_____

Name _____ Date _____

UNIT 5 What is the human spirit?

Reading 1: "Alone on a Raft"

Vocabulary   **Key Words** *Use with Student Edition page 249.*

Write each Key Word in the box next to its definition.

| conditions | experiences | fortunately | incredible | rescued | survive |

Example: __rescued__: saved from a dangerous situation

1. _____: things you do, or happen to you

2. _____: very good, or hard to believe

3. _____: continue living

4. _____: circumstances or state of something

5. _____: luckily; by good fortune

6. It is very difficult to _____ in the desert without water.

7. The weather _____ were so bad that it was impossible to travel.

8. My father found a ladder and _____ the kitten from the tree.

9. _____, everyone was able to finish the race before it started raining.

10. Both good and bad _____ shape our lives.

11. Climbing Mount Everest was one of the most _____ experiences of her life.

Unit 5 • Reading 1   129

Vocabulary — Academic Words *Use with Student Edition page 250.*

Read the paragraph below. Pay attention to the underlined Academic Words.

> A trade union is a group of workers who bargain together to improve their wages, benefits, and working conditions. The idea behind a union is that workers who stand together have a stronger impact. One of the best-known unions is The American Federation of Labor. It was founded in 1886 by Samuel Gompers. Its first aim was to protect the safety of workers who performed manual labor. Gompers' persistence led to better pay, shorter hours, and more job security for all union members.

Write the letter of the correct definition next to each Academic Word.

Example: __c__ remarkable

_____ 1. aspect   a. one part of something that has many parts

_____ 2. persistence   b. determination to do something even though it is difficult or other people oppose it

_____ 3. impact   c. amazing and worthy of attention

d. effect that an event or situation has on someone or something

Use the Academic Words from the exercise above to complete the sentences.

4. "Alone on a Raft" is a _____ story of survival.

5. The speech had a great _____ on everyone who heard it.

6. Which _____ of the story did you find most interesting?

7. He didn't know the answer right away, but with his _____, he finally got it.

Complete the sentences with your own ideas.

Example: Students who show great persistence __often do well in school__.

8. The last experience that had a great impact on me was _____.

9. One of the most remarkable things I've ever seen was _____.

10. For me, the most difficult aspect of English is _____.

Name _____ Date _____

Word Study   Capitalization *Use with Student Edition page 251.*

> **REMEMBER** Capitalize the word *I*, the first letter of the first word in a sentence, all proper nouns, names, and titles of people. Also capitalize geographical terms (and streets, cities, states, countries, continents), historical events (eras, calendar items), and the names of ethnic groups, national groups, and languages.

Look at the chart below. Capitalize each word correctly. Write the correct word in the chart. Then write the rule.

Incorrect Capitalization	Correct Capitalization	Rule
Today i walk the dog.	I	*Capitalize I.*
1. The moon is full tonight.		
2. My father is dr. lee.		
3. We visit the grand canyon.		
4. Tomorrow is new year's eve.		
5. Risa studies spanish.		

Look at the sentences below. Write corrected sentences on the lines.

Example: a new chinese restaurant opened on main street.

    A new Chinese restaurant opened on Main Street.

6. the red cross, a health group, went to haiti where many people speak french.

_____

7. we study the european renaissance and enlightenment in mr. smith's class.

_____

8. i live at 22 vine avenue in london, england.

_____

9. the empire state building and the statue of liberty are located in new york city.

_____

10. my birthday is on the fourth monday in april, the same as earth day.

_____

Reading Strategy: Identify Main Idea and Details

Use with Student Edition page 251.

REMEMBER When you read, identify the main idea and details. The main idea is the most important idea in the text. The details are pieces of information that support the main idea. The main idea may be at the beginning, in the middle, or at the end of a paragraph.

Read the paragraph and answer the questions below.

Don't panic if you realize you are lost. Find or build a shelter before nightfall. Gather wood and light a fire. Take inventory of everything that you have with you. These are a few survival tips if you get lost in the wilderness.

1. In what sentence is the main idea of the paragraph?

2. What is the main idea of the paragraph?

3. How many details are provided that support the main idea? What are they?

4. How can the strategy of identifying the main idea and details help you become a better reader?

Comprehension *Use with Student Edition page 258.*

Choose the best answer for each item. Circle the letter of the correct answer.

1. Conditions for workers on merchant ships were _____ on passenger ships.

   a. better than   b. worse than   c. about the same as

2. The *Ben Lomond* was sunk by a _____ submarine.

   a. Chinese   b. German   c. British

3. A _____ helped Poon Lim survive immediately after the sinking.

   a. life jacket   b. canvas roof   c. life raft

4. Poon Lim spent about _____ months on his raft.

   a. 4   b. 3   c. 2

5. After his rescue, Poon Lim eventually moved to _____.

   a. Brazil   b. the United States c. England

Extension *Use with Student Edition page 259.*

We read about many of the challenges Poon Lim faced in this remarkable survival story. Write a paragraph about some of the other challenges you imagine he faced that weren't mentioned in the story.

_____
_____
_____
_____
_____

Unit 5 • Reading 1

Grammar: Inseparable Phrasal Verbs *Use with Student Edition page 260.*

REMEMBER A phrasal verb is made up of a verb and one or more prepositions. The meaning of a phrasal verb differs from the meaning of the original verb.
Example: I try to work out at the gym every day. *Work* means *to labor*, but the phrasal verb *work out* means *to exercise*.
When a phrasal verb is inseparable, a noun or pronoun cannot be placed between the verb and the preposition that follows it.
Example: She dropped out of the race.
Notice that *the race* must follow the phrasal verb *dropped out of*.

Underline the phrasal verb in each sentence below.

Example: My mother <u>works out</u> every day.

1. He got into the back seat of the car.
2. She was not feeling well, and yesterday she came down with a cold.
3. When you are walking, hold on to the handrail so that you do not fall.
4. We went over our tests in class so we could see our mistakes.
5. It was hard to catch up with Cyrus. He ran very fast.

Read the definitions of each phrasal verb in parentheses. Then write a sentence with the phrasal verb. (Some phrasal verbs have more than one meaning. Use the meaning that is given here.)

Example: (wait up for = stay awake until someone arrives)

Whenever I go out in the evening, my mother waits up for me.

6. (look after = take care of someone)

   _____

7. (come across = find something accidentally or unexpectedly)

   _____

8. (not give in = not stop fighting)

   _____

Name _____ Date _____

Separable Phrasal Verbs *Use with Student Edition page 261.*

> **REMEMBER** When a phrasal verb is separable, the object can either follow the preposition or come between the verb and preposition. When the object is a pronoun, it must come between the verb and preposition.
> **Examples:** Please *bring back* your library book. Please *bring* it *back*.

Circle the best definition for each underlined separable phrasal verb.

Example: She <u>called</u> the party <u>off</u>. She was sick.

    (a.) canceled   b. held

1. The teacher <u>gave</u> our tests <u>back</u>.

    a. took   b. returned

2. Can <u>I get back</u> my book? I'd really like to read it.

    a. give   b. receive

3. Brett has <u>set up</u> a website where you can see his photos.

    a. closed   b. arranged

4. She <u>turned off</u> the TV.

    a. started   b. stopped

Rewrite the sentences in the exercise above, placing the object either between the preposition and the verb or after the preposition.

Example: *She called off the party.*

5. _____

6. _____

7. _____

8. _____

Unit 5 • Reading 1

Writing Write a Letter to the Editor

Use with Student Edition pages 262–263.

Complete your own graphic organizer for an issue you feel strongly about in your school or community. Start by listing your main idea. Next, write a topic sentence that expresses your main idea. Finally, list as many details as you can that support the main idea.

Main Idea:		
Topic Sentence:		
Detail:	Detail:	Detail:

Use the Peer Review Checklist below to obtain feedback from your partner. This feedback will help you edit your final draft.

Peer Review Checklist

☐ Does your topic sentence clearly express your main idea?

☐ Do your details support your main idea?

☐ Will your topic sentence and details help your reader understand the key points you are trying to make?

Name _____ Date _____

UNIT 5 — What is the human spirit?

Reading 2: From *"Three Letters: A Play in One Act"*

Vocabulary — Literary Words Use with Student Edition page 265.

> **REMEMBER** A **drama** is a play that is performed by actors. It consists of dialogue and **stage directions**. Stage directions describe the action and environment onstage. They are often printed in italics or brackets.

Read each sentence in the chart. Imagine that you are reading a drama. Write *stage directions* if you think the sentence is part of the drama's stage direction. Write *dialogue* if you think the sentence is part of the drama's dialogue.

Dialogue or Stage Directions?	Description
stage directions	*Paula held the jewel up to the light.*
1.	What do you mean by that?
2.	I think it's time I should be leaving.
3.	*There's a loud noise outside the window.*

Read the following excerpt from a play.

> MIKE: [*angrily*] Give it back, Ty! I'm warning you.
> TY: Mike, you know I didn't take Ana's letter. [*Sighing*] I would never do that.
>   [*Ty reaches out a hand to Mike, who refuses to take it.*]
> MIKE: Well if you didn't take it, who did? The cat?
>   [*Ty's cat walks across the stage in a purple spotlight. They watch it go.*]
> TY: Somehow I doubt it, Mike.
>   [*After a moment they both smile.*]

4. Underline the names of the speakers, and circle the stage directions.

5. Write two more lines of dialogue for the scene between Mike and Ty.

_____

_____

Vocabulary Academic Words *Use with Student Edition page 266.*

Read the paragraph below. Pay attention to the underlined Academic Words.

> Our school has a student handbook for new students. The handbook has information about the school and lists <u>regulations</u> that students must obey. It also lists rules about how to behave when entering and leaving school. For example, we are not supposed to make noise in front of the school, as this would disturb the <u>occupants</u> of the apartment building next door. Though the handbook contains a lot of information, it has <u>assisted</u> many new students in adjusting to our school. You can <u>correspond</u> with the school, and we'll be happy to send you a copy.

Write the Academic Words from the paragraph above next to their correct definitions.

Example: *regulations*: official rules or orders

1. _____: helped someone

2. _____: communicate in written form

3. _____: people who live in a building, room, etc.

Use the Academic Words from the exercise above to complete the sentences.

4. Nowadays, people often _____ electronically rather than on paper.

5. The tutor _____ me with my homework.

6. The _____ of the apartment weren't home when we visited.

7. In the lab, it's important to follow safety _____ so you don't get hurt.

Complete the sentences with your own ideas.

Example: The older students have assisted the *incoming students*.

8. Some people like to correspond because _____.

9. The occupants of my home are _____.

10. In my school there are important regulations to follow, such as _____.

Name _____ Date _____

Word Study — Antonyms *Use with Student Edition page 267.*

REMEMBER Antonyms are words that have opposite or nearly opposite meanings. For example, *near* is an antonym for *far*. Learning antonyms helps you express your exact meaning and figure out the meaning of words you do not know.

Look at the chart below. Write an antonym for each word. Use a thesaurus or a dictionary if needed.

Words	Antonym
ending	*beginning*
1. friend	
2. distant	
3. optimistic	
4. defeat	
5. agitated	

Look at the chart below. Write an antonym for each word. Then write a sentence using the antonym. Use a thesaurus or a dictionary if needed.

Word	Antonym	Sentence
courageous	cowardly	*The cowardly lion ran from the mouse.*
6. expensive		
7. early		
8. succeed		
9. generous		
10. enormous		

Unit 5 • Reading 2

Reading Strategy: Read Aloud

Use with Student Edition page 267.

REMEMBER Learning to read aloud brings a story and characters to life.

Read each passage. Then answer the questions.

Lucy: Remember when we had that big fight?
Jenna: I'm sorry about that. I didn't mean those things I said.
Lucy: I forgive you, because it's important to forgive your friends, right?
Jenna: Right!
Lucy: Then I hope you'll forgive me, because I just crashed your bike.

1. If you were reading Jenna's first line, what emotion would you show?

2. If you were reading Lucy's last line, what emotion would you show?

Papa: You can't go to the party and that's final.
Julio: But you said I could go!
Papa: That's before I found out that the party is 100 miles away!
Julio: That's so unfair!

3. If you were reading Papa's lines, what emotion would be in your voice?

4. How does the punctuation in this passage help you to know how to read Julio's lines?

5. How do you think the strategy of reading aloud with expression will make you a better reader?

Comprehension — Use with Student Edition page 276.

Choose the *best* answer for each item. Circle the letter of the correct answer.

1. The Ito family is living in a _____.

   a. barracks   b. house   c. barn

2. The family used to grow _____.

   a. tea   b. strawberries   c. tomatoes

3. The first letter in the play tells the Ito family that they have lost their _____.

   a. house   b. son   c. farmland

4. Louise's brother George is a(n) _____.

   a. soldier   b. MP   c. doctor

5. Yoshiko changes her mind about going to _____.

   a. the post office   b. the garden   c. the jazz concert

Response to Literature — Use with Student Edition page 277.

The Ito family was forced to leave their farm in California during World War II and live in an internment camp. They lived in a barracks with many other families. They couldn't leave the camp and had many rules to follow. There were soldiers and guard towers. Try to imagine living in those conditions. In the space below, write a short paragraph describing how that might feel.

_____
_____
_____
_____
_____

Unit 5 • Reading 2

Grammar: Present Past Perfect *Use with Student Edition page 278.*

REMEMBER Use the present perfect to describe an action that began in the past and continues into the present. The present perfect is formed with *have* or *has* + the past participle of a verb. Use the past perfect to tell about events that happened at an unspecified time in the past. When the simple past is used with the past perfect, the clause in the past perfect tells about the event that happened first. Form the past perfect with *had* + the past participle. When *for* is used with the present or past perfect, it specifies how long an activity has or had been going on. When *since* is used with the present or past perfect, it specifies the exact point in time when an activity began. Use adverbs such as *just, yet, already, ever, before,* and *never* to show different time orders.

Circle the correct word to complete each sentence.

Example: I can watch TV now. I (have / had) finished my homework.

1. We've lived here (for / since) 2017.
2. He (has / had) eaten dinner before he went to the party.
3. She had worked there (for / since) three years when she changed jobs.
4. Have you (ever / before) visited France?
5. She called her mother after the movie (has / had) finished.

Answer each question with information about yourself, using the present or past perfect.

Example: How long have you studied English? <u>I've studied English for two years</u>.

6. Where had you studied before you came to this school?
   _____.

7. What are some interesting places that you've visited?
   _____.

8. What had you already done today before you came to class?
   _____.

Name _____ Date _____

Factual and Unreal Conditionals *Use with Student Edition page 279.*

> **REMEMBER** A conditional sentence has an *if*-clause that presents a condition and a result clause that tells what may or may not happen if the condition is met. Look at the examples.

Present Factual: The condition may be true in the present.	**If** a disease spreads, people **get** sick. **When** a storm hits, we **stay** indoors.
Future Factual: The condition may be true in the future.	**If** your house floods, where **will** you **go**?
Present Unreal: The condition is not true in the present.	If he **didn't enlist**, he was afraid of what **would happen** to his family.
Past Unreal: The condition was not true in the past.	If he **hadn't been** a translator, he **would have had** to go to the front.

Complete the conditional sentences with the correct form of the verb in parentheses.

Example: If you come with me, we ____'ll have____ (have) a good time.

1. When it's cold, she _____ (wear) a hat.

2. If he hadn't lost his keys, he _____ (pick) us up.

3. If I _____ (study) all the time, I would fail this class.

4. What would happen if you _____ (stay) out all night?

5. If we hadn't met at that party, we _____ (be) friends now.

6. What do you think you _____ (do) when you graduate?

7. If you give him money, he _____ (spend) it.

8. If he _____ (cause) so much trouble, I would invite him to the party.

Unit 5 • Reading 2 143

Writing Write a Persuasive Paragraph

Use with Student Edition pages 280–281.

Complete your own pros-and-cons chart for a paragraph on an issue you feel strongly about.

Pros	Cons

Use the Peer Review Checklist below to obtain feedback from your partner. This feedback will help you edit your final draft.

Peer Review Checklist
- ☐ Is the main issue clearly presented?
- ☐ Is the writer's opinion clearly stated?
- ☐ Does the writer give supporting reasons for this opinion?
- ☐ Are both sides of the argument presented?
- ☐ Does the writer give reasons for disagreeing with the opposing arguments?
- ☐ Are present perfect and present perfect progressive used correctly?
- ☐ What changes could be made to improve the paragraph?

Name _____ Date _____

UNIT 5: What is the human spirit?

Reading 3: "A Place in the World"

Vocabulary — **Literary Words** Use with Student Edition page 283.

> **REMEMBER** A **dialogue** is a conversation between characters. Dialogue is shown with quotation marks. Quotation marks let you know which character is speaking and how the dialogue should be read. The **theme** is a central message in a story. Usually it is not stated directly. You must decide what the theme is by looking closely at the work.

Read each sentence below. If a sentence contains dialogue, write *yes* in the space provided. If a sentence does not contain dialogue, write *no* in the space provided.

Dialogue?	Sentence
yes	Darrell said, "You should come to dinner with Jen and me."
1.	"I've been listening to this song all day," she said, grinning.
2.	We told them we would show up later in the evening.
3.	It's always been easy for her.
4.	I responded, "I don't think it exists."

Read the dialogue below. Answer the question below.

"How are you doing?" Sarah asked, sitting beside Leah.
"Not great!" Leah replied. "I haven't finished my work and it's so late." She sighed.
Sarah smiled helpfully. "Would you like me to stay up a while with you?" she asked.
Leah beamed back. "Thanks, I really could use some help."
"Excellent!" Sarah said. "I'll make cocoa."

5. What is one theme of the passage above? _____

Unit 5 • Reading 3   145

Vocabulary — Academic Words Use with Student Edition page 284.

Read the paragraph below. Pay attention to the underlined Academic Words.

> A very important <u>tradition</u> in my family is getting together for the holidays. Even though I live far away, my mother says that it's <u>crucial</u> I attend. This year, unfortunately, my city was hit with a terrible snowstorm and I was unable to travel. My mother said they would <u>alter</u> their plans and wait until I could attend, but I insisted they <u>proceed</u> as planned. "Well, okay," she finally agreed, "but it just won't be the same without you."

Example: ___*alter*___ : to make or cause a change

1. _____ : move forward or continue

2. _____ : a belief or custom that has existed for a long time

3. _____ : critical or extremely important

4. Maintaining the quality of our products is _____ for our success.

5. Circumstances have changed so we need to _____ some of our plans.

6. Honestly, I'm not quite sure how we should _____ .

7. In some families, it's a _____ to give thanks before each meal.

Example: Some animals are able to alter ___*their appearance*___ .

8. _____ is crucial for maintaining good health.

9. We've decided to proceed with _____ .

10. My favorite family tradition is _____ .

Name _____ Date _____

Word Study — Words Ending with Consonant + -le, -al, -el

Use with Student Edition page 285.

> **REMEMBER** In English, many words end with a consonant and -le as in *thimble*, -al as in *mental*, or -el as in *gavel*. There are no rules for spelling these words, so it's best to memorize the spelling for each.

Read the words in the box below. Then write each word in the correct column in the chart.

| ~~tickle~~ | lapel | rental | sample | |
| corral | dispel | hotel | example | oriental |

Consonant + -le	Consonant + -al	Consonant + -el
tickle		

Underline the two-word letter pattern at the end of each word below. Then write a sentence using the word. Use a dictionary if needed.

Examples: divisib<u>le</u> *Four, six, and eight are divisible by two.*

1. pickle _____

2. canal _____

3. capital _____

4. novel _____

5. sentimental _____

6. camel _____

7. candle _____

Unit 5 • Reading 3   147

Reading Strategy   Make Inferences

Use with Student Edition page 285.

> **REMEMBER** Drawing inferences helps you figure out information that an author does not give directly. As you read, think about the characters and the setting, as well as your own experiences.

Read each paragraph and answer the questions that follow.

When Libby's dad signed her up for the swim club, she was angry. The first day, she could swim only two laps, while kids half her age swam for hours without getting tired. But after the first month, she could swim twenty laps without stopping. When Libby told her dad that the coach wanted her to join a swim meet, he was surprised by her reaction.

1. What can you infer about Libby's reaction from the passage above?

   _____

   _____

2. What event from your own experience has helped you understand Libby's feelings?

   _____

   _____

Dan and Evan had been best friends since second grade, even though they were complete opposites. Dan loved sports. He played baseball, soccer, lacrosse, and football. Evan dreamed of being a famous movie director. Then Carlos moved into the house between the two boys. Carlos loved movies just as much as Evan did.

3. What can you infer about how Carlos' arrival may affect the friendship between Dan and Evan?

   _____

4. What event or knowledge from your own experience helped you to make an inference about the passage?

   _____

5. How do you think drawing inferences can help you to understand what you read better?

   _____

   _____

Comprehension *Use with Student Edition page 294.*

Choose the best answer for each item. Circle the letter of the correct answer.

1. The name of the hurricane was _____.

   a. Imelda   b. Rose   c. Miguel

2. Mrs. Moreno's kiosk was special because it _____.

   a. was in the best location in town   b. had the lowest-priced products

   c. was a tradition in the community

3. Mrs. Moreno loaned Miguel _____.

   a. a power cable   b. a binder clip   c. a packet of graph paper

4. Miguel's idea was to _____.

   a. rebuild Mrs. Moreno's kiosk   b. help Mrs. Moreno get a store

   c. raise money to buy a new kiosk

5. Miguel painted _____ on the back of the kiosk.

   a. "Thank You!"   b. the kiosk's name   c. a smiley face

Response to Literature *Use with Student Edition page 295.*

Imagine the scene at the end of "A Place in the World" when Mrs. Moreno sees her rebuilt kiosk for the first time. What does the kiosk look like? Who is there? How do the people feel? Draw a picture of the scene in the space below.

Grammar: Quoted Speech and Reported Speech

Use with Student Edition page 296.

REMEMBER Use quotation marks (" ") and a comma (,) to separate direct, or quoted, speech from the phrase that identifies the speaker. Reported speech does not use quotation marks and may be a paraphrase of the person's exact words. The verb form usually changes.

Change the sentences from quoted speech to reported speech, or from reported speech to quoted speech.

Example: "We can all help her," he said. _He said (that) they could all help her_.

1. She said that it was too expensive.

   _____

2. "Are you OK?" he asked.

   _____

3. They said (that) they weren't coming.

   _____

4. "The storm destroyed everything," she said.

   _____

5. He said (that) he could take me.

   _____

6. "I don't know where my keys are," my father said.

   _____

7. She answered (that) she really appreciated it.

   _____

8. "Can you come to the party?" Emery asked.

   _____

Name _____ Date _____

Present Perfect Progressive *Use with Student Edition page 297.*

> **REMEMBER** Use the present perfect progressive to emphasize the duration of an action that was in progress in the past and may continue into the present. *For, since,* and the phrases *all morning, all day long,* etc., signal the present perfect progressive. Form the present perfect progressive with *has* or *have* + *been* + the present participle.
> **Example:** He *has been studying* all morning. (He is still studying *or* he has just finished.)

Complete the sentences with the present perfect progressive form of the verb in parentheses. Then write whether the action *continues* or is *completed*.

Example: He __*has been working*__ (work) in this company since 1999.
 __*continues*__

1. I _____ (wait) for you since two o'clock. What took you so long? _____

2. Marta _____ (live) in Kiev since 2001. _____

3. He's tired because he _____ (play) handball for two hours. _____

4. We _____ (look) for the exit for an hour and still haven't found it. _____

5. How long _____ she _____ (work) in the garden? It's getting hot. _____

6. It _____ (snow) for hours and is still coming down. _____

7. They _____ (talk) for the last hour. _____

8. What _____ you _____ (do) for the last 20 minutes? _____

9. Jim _____ (teach) at the school for the last three years. _____

10. I _____ (exercise) a lot lately. _____

Unit 5 • Reading 3

Writing — **Write a Review** *Use with Student Edition pages 298–299.*

Complete your own idea web for a review of a book, play, or film.

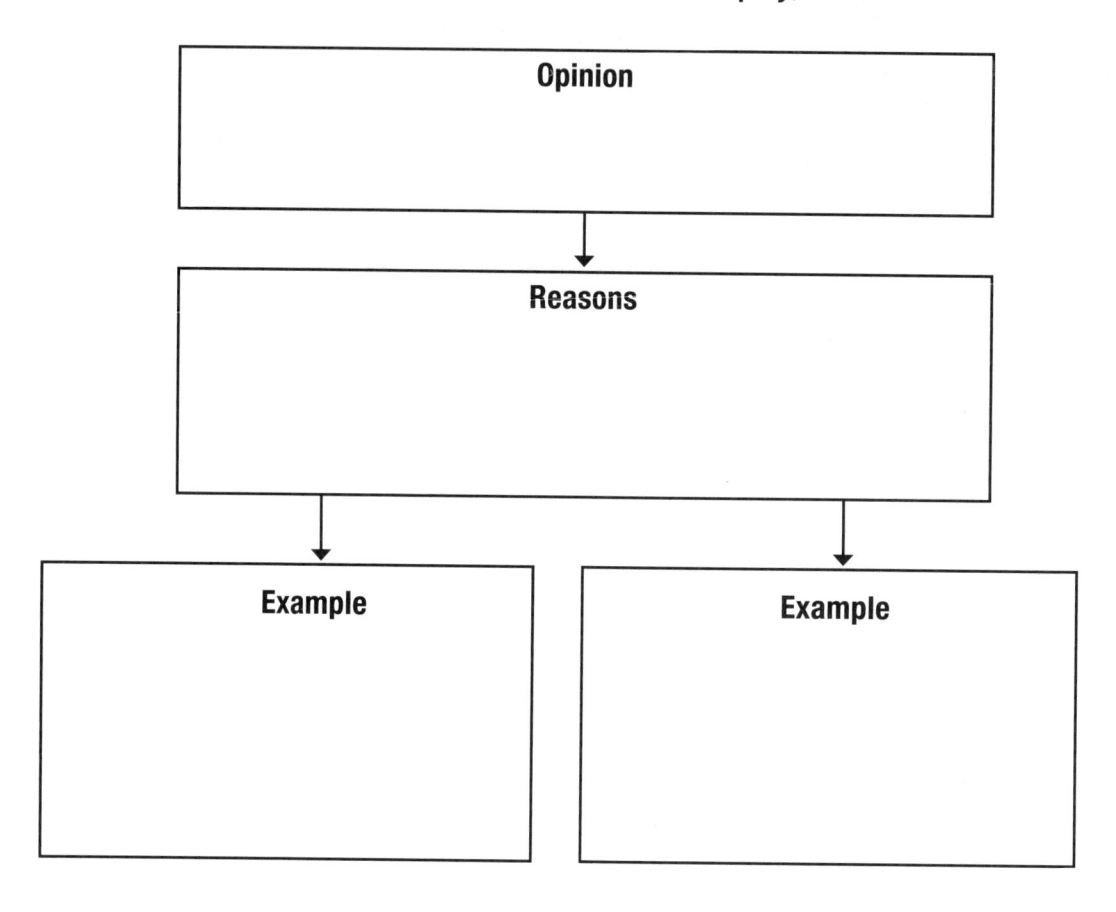

```
┌─────────────────────────────────────┐
│              Opinion                │
│                                     │
└─────────────────────────────────────┘
                  │
                  ▼
┌─────────────────────────────────────┐
│              Reasons                │
│                                     │
│                                     │
└─────────────────────────────────────┘
        │                    │
        ▼                    ▼
┌───────────────┐    ┌───────────────┐
│   Example     │    │   Example     │
│               │    │               │
│               │    │               │
└───────────────┘    └───────────────┘
```

Use the Peer Review Checklist below to obtain feedback from your partner. This feedback will help you edit your final draft.

Peer Review Checklist

☐ Does the paragraph include the main points of the film or book?
☐ Is the writer's opinion clearly stated?
☐ Is the writer's opinion supported with details and examples?
☐ Is punctuation used correctly?
☐ Is reported speech used correctly?
☐ What changes could be made to improve the paragraph?

Name _____ Date _____

Writing Workshop *Use with Student Edition pages 304–308.*

Organize your ideas in the graphic organizer below.

Pros	Cons

Use the Peer Review Checklist below to obtain feedback from your partner. This feedback will help you edit your final draft.

Peer Review Checklist

- ☐ Was the writer's opinion clearly presented?
- ☐ Was the opinion supported with details and facts?
- ☐ Did the writer present both sides of the argument?
- ☐ Did the writer give reasons for not agreeing with the opposing position?
- ☐ Did the concluding paragraph sum up the main points in a memorable way?
- ☐ What changes could be made to improve the essay?

Learning Log *Use after completing Student Edition page 308.*

Underline the vocabulary items you know and can use well. Review and practice any you haven't underlined. Underline them when you know them well.

Literary Words	Key Words	Academic Words
drama stage directions dialogue theme	conditions experiences fortunately incredible rescued survive	aspect impact persistence remarkable assisted correspond occupants regulations altered crucial proceed tradition

Put a check by the skills you can perform well. Review and practice any you haven't checked off. Check them off when you can perform them well.

Skills	I can . . .
Word Study	☐ recognize and spell capitalized words. ☐ recognize and spell words ending with consonant + -le, -al, and -el. ☐ recognize antonyms.
Reading Strategies	☐ make inferences. ☐ read aloud. ☐ identify the main idea and details.
Grammar	☐ use inseparable and separable phrasal verbs. ☐ use quoted speech and reported speech. ☐ use the present perfect progressive. ☐ use the present and past perfect. ☐ use factual and unreal conditionals.
Writing	☐ write a persuasive paragraph. ☐ write a letter to the editor. ☐ write a review.

Name _____ Date _____

Test Preparation

Test 1

DIRECTIONS
Read this selection. Then choose the best word to complete the sentences.

History Report

Today students are reading about what they will need to do to complete a report for a history class. The selection below is about preparing to present the report.

1   After you have finished your research, you are ready to create note cards. You will use the note cards to remind you of the information you found. This lets you talk about your __1__, instead of reading the entire report. This makes your presentation more interesting to listen to.

2   The note cards should each give an important fact about this __2__ in history. Add details about the fact on the card. Do not write in complete sentences. Just write phrases that will remind you of what to say.

3   After you write all of your note cards, put them in order. You can group your cards by __3__ ideas, or you can put them in time order. Make sure that the grouping of the ideas will make sense to your audience.

4   Practice giving your report more than once. You should speak for five minutes. If you cannot speak that long, you need more information in your report. If you do not know what to say about a fact, add more details to your note cards. Ask friends or adults to listen to your presentation. Then let them tell you if anything was __4__.

1   **A** person
    B project
    C present
    D public

2   **A** group
    B alarm
    C watch
    D period

3   **A** similar
    B interesting
    C faithful
    D concerned

4   **A** undone
    B unclear
    C unopened
    D untied

Test Preparation

Test 2

DIRECTIONS
Read this selection. Then answer the questions that follow it.

The Photographs of Dorothea Lange

1   Dorothea Lange's photographs help us see the world she saw. Lange photographed the world of everyday people with compassion and dedication. She showed how these people dealt with the problems they faced. Her depiction of ordinary people in difficult times has helped us understand the history of the United States.

2   She is especially known for her work during the Great Depression. She captured on film families escaping from Dust Bowl farms and migrating west in search of work. Her best-known picture, titled "Migrant Mother," shows a woman who kept her family alive on frozen vegetables taken from the field and birds captured by her children.

3   During World War II, Lange's work showed the effects of the war on the home front. She photographed the internment camps where Japanese Americans were relocated and held during the war. She showed workers, including women and minorities, at California shipyards.

4   Thanks to Lange's photographs, we can see today what she saw years ago; we can look directly at the human spirit of the past. More importantly, her vision helps us see our present-day world more clearly. As Lange said, "The camera is an instrument that teaches people how to see without a camera."

1 In paragraph 1, what words help the reader know what *depiction* means?
  A she showed
  B the problems
  C faced
  D compassion

2 Which sentence is an opinion?
  A *She photographed the internment camps where Japanese Americans were relocated and held during the war.*
  B *During World War II, Lange's work showed the effects of the war on the home front.*
  C *More importantly, her vision helps us see our present-day world more clearly.*
  D *She captured on film families escaping from Dust Bowl farms and migrating west in search of work.*

3 According to the article, what was one effect of World War II?
  A farmers migrating west
  B people searching for work
  C Japanese internment camps
  D migrating mothers

4 The article suggests that because of Lange's photographs —
  A people can appreciate how hard life is today
  B people today can understand how people of the past survived difficulties
  C people should use a camera in order to understand the past
  D photographers will continue to take pictures of events in history

Name _____ Date _____

Test 3

DIRECTIONS
Read this selection. Then answer the questions that follow it.

Roberto Clemente

1. Roberto Clemente was born in Puerto Rico in 1934. He was the youngest of seven children. As a child, Roberto loved playing baseball. Because his family didn't have much money, he used tree branches for bats. To make baseballs, he wrapped old golf balls in string and tape.

2. While in high school, Clemente began playing for a professional baseball team in Puerto Rico. Soon, the Los Angeles Dodgers spotted him and hired him to play for a minor league team. One year later, the Pittsburgh Pirates asked him to play for the major leagues. He played right field for the Pirates for eighteen years. During that time he won twelve Golden Glove awards and was voted Most Valuable Player.

3. Though Clemente spoke English, it was not perfect, and sports writers sometimes made fun of him. However, he was proud of his heritage. He did not let the sports writers make him feel ashamed of his traditions and history. He was also determined to help other native Spanish speakers. He helped many young Spanish-speaking baseball players and held baseball clinics for children in Puerto Rico.

4. In 1972, three strong earthquakes hit Nicaragua, killing thousands of people and leaving many homeless. Clemente and four others decided to help the victims by flying a plane to Nicaragua filled with medicine and supplies. His wife begged him not to go because she thought the trip was too dangerous. Unfortunately, she was right. The plane crashed into the ocean, killing all those on board.

5. After his death, Clemente became the first native Spanish speaker to be elected to the Baseball Hall of Fame. Though he died young, he gave a lot to the world during his lifetime.

1 How did Roberto Clemente help other native Spanish speakers?
   A He flew to Nicaragua to help victims of an earthquake.
   B He won the Golden Glove Award.
   C He was voted Most Valuable Player.
   D He held baseball clinics for children in Puerto Rico.

2 Paragraph 4 is mainly about —
   A how Roberto Clemente died
   B how Roberto Clemente helped native Spanish speakers
   C Roberto Clemente's wife
   D an earthquake in Nicaragua

3 In paragraph 3, what words help the reader know what *heritage* means?
   A for children
   B traditions and history
   C not perfect
   D feel ashamed

4 The reader can conclude that Roberto Clemente —
   A was a good baseball coach
   B was a talented baseball player
   C loved his wife and family
   D was stubborn

5 Which sentence in paragraph 4 shows that Roberto Clemente was kind?
   A *His wife begged him not to go because she thought the trip was too dangerous.*
   B *Unfortunately, she was right. The plane crashed into the ocean, killing all those on board.*
   C *In 1972, three strong earthquakes hit Nicaragua, killing thousands and leaving many homeless.*
   D *Roberto and four others decided to help the victims by flying a plane to Nicaragua filled with medicine and supplies.*

Name _____ Date _____

Visual Literacy: Smithsonian American
Art Museum *Use with Student Edition pages 310–311.*

Learning to Look

Look at *Spirit of Life* by Daniel Chester French on page 311 in your Student Edition. Describe six things you see in this sculpture. State facts, not opinions.

Example: The figure has wings.

1. _____
2. _____
3. _____
4. _____
5. _____
6. _____

Interpretation

Look at *Fan Quilt, Mt. Carmel* by the Residents of Bourbon County, Kentucky, on page 310 in your textbook. Imagine that you are helping them to make the quilt. Recreate a conversation they might have had. Include yourself as a character!

Example: This is so time consuming, but I love to sew with different colors.

_____
_____
_____
_____
_____
_____
_____

KWLH

Look at *Speaking to Hear* by Michael Olszewski on page 311 in your Student Edition. Use that artwork to complete the KWLH Chart below.

K	W	L	H
What do you **know** about using fabric in art?	What do you **want** to learn about this work of art?	What have you **learned** about using fabric in art from looking at this work?	**How** have you learned about fabric in art?

Name _____ Date _____

UNIT 6 How does the sky influence us?

Reading 1: "The Girl Who Married the Moon"

Vocabulary — **Literary Words** *Use with Student Edition page 315.*

> **REMEMBER** A **myth** is a short fictional tale that explains the origins of elements of nature. It has been passed from generation to generation by storytellers. Sometimes myths use **personification**, which gives human qualities to nonhuman animals or things.

Read each sentence. Write *yes* if it uses personification. Write *no* if it does not use personification.

Personification?	Sentences
yes	The house stood watchfully at the end of the lane.
1.	The roof pointed toward the sky.
2.	The city came alive, stretching its limbs, beginning to speak morning words.
3.	There's a sense of humor to the moonlight tonight. It's as if the Moon wants us to stay out a little later.

Read the short myth and answer the questions that follow.

> The face of the Moon is a mirror. It's carried across the sky by a family, whose skin is so pale and delicate that they can only come out at night, so they don't get burned. The family members pull the Moon across the sky. They look at Earth in the mirror. That way they remember where they came from. The <u>smiling face</u> in the Moon belongs to the person carrying the Moon. The stars twinkle at them in greeting. And the ocean waters wave and say hello when the Moon floats by.

4. Underline the words and phrases that personify nonhuman objects or animals.

5. What natural phenomena does the myth try to explain?

_____

Unit 6 • Reading 1

Vocabulary — **Academic Words** *Use with Student Edition page 316.*

Read the paragraph below. Pay attention to the underlined Academic Words.

> My first job was babysitting for a family with two children named Haley and Jack. At first I thought the children were well-behaved and compatible. Haley was still a baby, and her parents instructed me how to change her diaper. I was told their older child Jack was restricted from watching television after 8:00 p.m. Jack did not like when I told him it was time to go to bed. He ignored me and kept watching television. The first night babysitting was hard. However, my mom says it is just a phase and that I will get used to babysitting soon.

Write the letter of the correct definition next to each word.

Example: __d__ job   a. able to exist together without problems

_____ 1. compatible   b. one stage of a process of change

_____ 2. instructed   c. taught or showed someone how to do something

_____ 3. phase   d. a particular duty or responsibility that you have

Use the Academic Words from the exercise above to complete the sentences.

4. Our grandmother _____ us how to play the game of bridge.

5. Each _____ of the moon lasts about one week.

6. His boring summer _____ was not much fun.

7. The teacher sat the students together because they seemed _____.

Complete the sentences with your own ideas.

Example: __My dad_____ instructed me to get out of bed early.

8. In my family, I am most compatible with _____.

9. My ideal job would be _____.

10. The moon phase I like best is _____.

162   Unit 6 • Reading 1

Name _____ Date _____

Word Study — Spelling Long *i* *Use with Student Edition page 317.*

REMEMBER The long *i* sound can be spelled several different ways. These include *i_e* as in *side*, *igh* as in *tight*, *y* as in *my*, and *i* as in *kind*. Knowing these patterns will help you spell words with the long *i* sound correctly.

Read the words in the box below. Then write each word in the correct column in the chart.

| while | style | isle | tonight | worthwhile | supply |
| grind | tightly | versatile | blind | blight | July |

Long i spelled *i_e*	Long i spelled *igh*	Long i spelled *y*	Long i spelled *i*
while			

Write the letter-sound pattern for long *i* in each word below.

Examples: might   <u>long /i/ spelled igh</u>

1. island   _____
2. sign   _____
3. slice   _____
4. simplify   _____
5. sprite   _____
6. sigh   _____
7. rind   _____
8. unify   _____

Unit 6 • Reading 1

Reading Strategy | **Read For Enjoyment** | *Use with Student Edition page 317.*

> **REMEMBER** When you read for enjoyment, you aren't just reading for information. You are reading to be entertained by other things, such as the characters, the setting, or the pictures that go with the text.

Read the passage. Then answer the questions that follow.

Anne of Green Gables is one of the most famous fictional characters in English literature. One of the best things about her is that she is not perfect. She has several things she can't stand about herself, including her plain name (she adds the "e" to the end of "Ann" to make it seem fancier) and her bright red hair. She is always getting in trouble. But although the book was published in 1908, it is still popular. In fact, thousands of people still visit Canada's Prince Edward Island just to see where Anne was supposed to live!

1. What qualities do you think make a great character?

   _____

   _____

2. Who is your favorite fictional character? Why?

   _____

   _____

3. What is your favorite setting in a novel or story you've read?

   _____

   _____

4. What is the name of the book that you have most enjoyed reading? Why?

   _____

   _____

5. When you read for pleasure, what sorts of texts do you choose to read? Write the name of one book you would like to read for pleasure.

   _____

   _____

Comprehension Use with Student Edition page 326.

Choose the best answer for each item. Circle the letter of the correct answer.

1. The two cousins could have married almost anyone but they fell in love with _____.

    a. the stars   b. the sun   c. the Moon

2. The Moon wanted a wife who was very _____.

    a. patient   b. pretty   c. quiet

3. After awhile, the Moon's wife became _____.

    a. bored   b. sad   c. content

4. The people lying facedown on the trail were _____.

    a. suns   b. stars   c. more moons

5. The Moon decided to let his wife _____.

    a. rest at home   b. carry pieces of Moon   c. watch the sun rise with him

Response to Literature Use with Student Edition page 327.

Find a chart showing the Moon in orbit around Earth. What part of the lunar cycle is carried by the Moon? What part is carried by his wife? Draw your own diagram to show the answers.

Unit 6 • Reading 1

Grammar — Prepositions Use with Student Edition page 328.

REMEMBER Prepositions such as *at* and *in* can be used to show time; they answer *When?*
In, *to*, and *from* can be used to show place; they answer *Where?*
By, *with*, *from*, *for*, and *of* can be used to provide details; they answer *How?* or *Why?*
A preposition is always followed by a noun or noun phrase. This is called a prepositional phrase.

Underline the prepositional phrase in each sentence. Then write the question that each answers: *When? Where? How?* or *Why?*

Example: The team scored another point <u>by stealing the ball</u>. ____How?____.

1. He got to school at 8:45. _____
2. The old man rose slowly from the chair. _____
3. I was calling with my cell phone. _____
4. The doors were locked with a deadbolt. _____
5. He spoke softly into the phone. _____

Complete each sentence with one of the prepositions from the box.

in	to	from	for	of	at

Example: He lived ____in____ New York for many years.

6. Several _____ the people had left.
7. He left the office _____ five o'clock.
8. We learned English _____ a native speaker.
9. They are going _____ Berlin this summer.
10. My father worked _____ the Peace Corps when he was young.

Name _____ Date _____

More about Antecedent / Pronoun Agreement *Use with Student Edition page 329.*

REMEMBER All pronouns must agree in number and gender with their antecedents. For example, if the antecedent is a singular, feminine noun, the pronouns must also be singular and feminine.
Example: *Deirdre* locked *herself* out of *her* car.
A generic noun refers to a whole group; it does not have a gender since it does not refer to anything in particular. When a singular generic noun refers to a person, use any singular pronoun that names a person. When a singular generic noun refers to a thing, use a neutral pronoun. When a generic noun is plural, use a plural pronoun.
Examples: When *a child* cries, *she* usually wants *her* mother.
Something fell, but I don't know what *it* was.
People always like to hear *themselves* talk.

Circle all the correct pronouns to complete each sentence.

Example: A student should always do (**his**) / (**her**) / its) homework.

1. Somebody left (his / its / her) cell phone in the cafeteria.

2. The cat ran under the fence, and (it / he / they) ran up a tree.

3. I get worried when the neighbors let (its / his / their) dog out.

4. Everyone needs to pick up (his / her / my) own trash.

5. Paul and I are riding (his / our / her) bikes through the park.

6. Even though the party was fun, (he / they / it) was crowded.

7. When a person has a car accident, (I / he / she) should pull off the road.

8. Katie and Adam are concerned about (his / her / their) grades.

Unit 6 • Reading 1

Grammar: Capitalization and Punctuation of Titles

Use with Student Edition page 330.

> **REMEMBER** Titles of short stories, short poems, myths, legends, songs, interviews, and informational texts are enclosed in quotation marks. Titles of novels, collections of stories, long poems, plays, paintings, movies, magazines, and newspapers are italicized. When writing by hand, you can show italics by underlining the title. If the title has a subtitle, use a colon after the title and capitalize the subtitle.
> **Example:** Don McLean's song "Vincent" was inspired by Van Gogh's *Starry Night*.

Circle the title in each sentence. Then write each title in the space provided, correcting the capitalization and punctuation.

Example: My little sister got scared watching (the wizard of oz.) _The Wizard of Oz_

1. The only magazine my mother reads is rolling stone. _____

2. Our class is going to see romeo and juliet. _____

3. We sang the Beatles' song hard day's night at the recital. _____

4. We read the road not taken in our poetry class. _____

5. Have you seen harry potter on Blu-ray? _____

6. We get the new york times delivered to our door. _____

7. My parents have a copy of Renoir's painting two sisters. _____

8. My mom gave me a collection of short stories called oddly enough. _____

Name _____ Date _____

Punctuation: Hyphens and Dashes *Use with Student Edition page 331.*

> **REMEMBER** A hyphen (-) is used within words. For example, a two-word adjective before a noun is hyphenated. Hyphens are also used with compound words.
> Dashes are longer than hyphens (—) and are used between words. There are no spaces before or after a dash. A pair of dashes is used to draw attention to an interruption in a sentence. Use a single dash to set off an appositive.
> **Example:** He didn't like the gift I gave him—a long-sleeved T-shirt.

Add hyphens to the adjectives and compound nouns in the following sentences.

Example: I got a sixty-six on my test.

1. She turns twenty three tomorrow.

2. James is a well known soccer player.

3. My neighbor is a very kind hearted man.

4. Have you responded to my e mail?

Add dashes to set off interruptions or appositives in the following sentences.

Example: Pam sat—alone and by herself—in the corner.

5. Greg ran quickly the quickest he'd ever run before.

6. The cat fat and lazy slept on the sofa as the mouse ran by.

7. The child went everywhere with her teddy bear worn and tattered as it was.

8. My brother as much as I love him drives me crazy sometimes.

Unit 6 • Reading 1

Writing: Include Paraphrases and Citations

Use with Student Edition pages 332–333.

Complete your own source chart listing citations for a paragraph about a myth.

Paraphrase	Source

Use the Peer Review Checklist below to obtain feedback from your partner. This feedback will help you edit your final draft.

Peer Review Checklist

- ☐ Is the main idea clearly presented?
- ☐ Is the main idea supported with details?
- ☐ Is information from sources paraphrased to support the main idea?
- ☐ Are in-text citations provided?
- ☐ Are sources cited correctly?
- ☐ Are capitalization and punctuation used correctly?
- ☐ What changes could be made to improve the paragraph?

Name _____ Date _____

UNIT 6: How does the sky influence us?

Reading 2: "Starry Nights" / "Stars" / "Escape at Bedtime"

Vocabulary — **Literary Words** *Use with Student Edition page 335.*

REMEMBER A **stanza** is a group of lines in a poem, usually similar in length and pattern. Stanzas are separated by spaces. **Rhyme** is the repetition of sounds at the ends of words. The lines in a stanza sometimes rhyme. **Rhyme scheme** is the pattern of the rhyme.

Read each pair of lines. Write *yes* if the lines rhyme. Write *no* if the lines do not rhyme. (Words with similar spellings may not have the same sound.)

Rhyme?	Lines
yes	The snow is very nice But I detest the ice
1.	Lush as a peach, twice as smooth
2.	The passing of time is quick and sublime
3.	Her love was a lamp Illuminating my heart
4.	Alone, in despair He sat in his chair

5. Write a stanza of a poem that has four rhyming lines.

_____

_____

_____

_____

Unit 6 • Reading 2

Vocabulary   **Academic Words** *Use with Student Edition page 336.*

Read the paragraph below. Pay attention to the underlined Academic Words.

> Jackson Pollock was a famous painter. He didn't paint realistic <u>images</u> of people, places, or things. He created paintings by pouring and dripping paint all over a canvas placed on the floor. Each drip and splash is a visible record of how he created the picture. Many art lovers and critics have tried to <u>analyze</u> the meaning behind Pollock's work. One interpretation is that it represents the artist's need to let go and create freely. Like a writer using different poetic <u>devices</u>, Pollock used different artistic <u>elements</u> to create his work.

Write the letter of the correct definition next to each word.

Example: ___c___ analyze   **a.** important parts of a whole system that work together to tell a story or create a feeling

_____ 1. devices   **b.** a picture that you can see through a camera, on a television, in a mirror, etc.

_____ 2. elements   **c.** examine or think about something carefully in order to understand it

_____ 3. image   **d.** how words are used in literature to achieve an effect

Use the Academic Words from the exercise above to complete the sentences.

4. The _____ on the movie screen was twenty feet high.

5. The students included different poetic _____ in the assignment.

6. The author used four different _____ of poetry in the selection.

7. The scientists took three months to _____ the data from the satellite.

Complete the sentences with your own ideas.

Example: His stories analyze the way people <u>show their love</u>.

8. I'll always remember the image of _____.

9. A poet can use poetic devices to _____.

10. Some elements of the painting include _____.

Name _____ Date _____

Word Study — Lexical Sets *Use with Student Edition page 337.*

REMEMBER Words that describe one main idea are called *lexical sets*. For instance, the lexical set for *easy* can include *simple*, *effortless*, *straightforward*, and *uncomplicated*. Knowing lexical sets can help you use the precise word you need to convey your meaning.

Look at the chart below. Underline the word that is <u>not</u> part of the lexical set. Use a dictionary if needed.

Word	Word	Word	Word
common	familiar	usual	<u>exotic</u>
1. casual	formal	mellow	easygoing
2. surprising	startling	unanticipated	predictable
3. clean	spotless	tidy	grimy
4. sour	tart	sugary	bitter
5. interesting	dull	appealing	fascinating

Write two or more words for each lexical set. Use a dictionary or thesaurus if needed.

Example: difficult   hard, tough

6. exciting   _____

7. unusual   _____

8. cheap   _____

9. nice   _____

10. boring   _____

Unit 6 • Reading 2

Reading Strategy — Analyze Text Structure and Elements of Poetry

Use with Student Edition page 337.

> **REMEMBER** Analyzing text structure can help you understand what kind of text you're reading. It can also help you set a purpose for reading. Remember that poems have a special text structure. They are arranged in lines and groups of lines called stanzas. Punctuation doesn't always follow the same rules in poetry as it does in other types of text.

Read the poems by Christina Rossetti. Then answer the questions.

53
If stars dropped out of heaven,
And if flowers took their place,
The sky would still look very fair,
And fair earth's face.

Winged angels might fly down to us
To pluck the stars,
But we would only long for flowers
Beyond the cloudy bars.

55
What do the stars do
Up in the sky,
Higher than the winds can blow,
Or the clouds can fly?

Each star in its own glory
Circles, circles still;
As it was lit to shine and set,
And do its Maker's will.

1. What is usually the purpose of reading poems? _____

2. Are there any rhyming lines in either poem? If so, what are they? _____

3. How are the poems similar? _____

4. What different perspectives about stars do the poems give you? _____

5. How can the strategy of analyzing text structure help you become a better reader? _____

Comprehension *Use with Student Edition page 342.*

Choose the best answer for each item. Circle the letter of the correct answer.

1. In the poem "Stars," Sara Teasdale describes the stars as _____.

    a. friendly and close   b. angry and fearsome   c. distant and amazing

2. The final stanza of Teasdale's poem focuses on _____.

    a. an early morning sky   b. a city cafe at night   c. the way stars make her feel

3. In "Escape at Bedtime," Stevenson rhymes every _____.

    a. two lines   b. three lines   c. four lines

4. Van Gogh felt that most paintings of nighttime scenes did not capture night's _____.

    a. loudness   b. darkness   c. colors

5. Unlike many other painters who worked on nighttime scenes, van Gogh _____.

    a. painted at night   b. used mainly black paint   c. painted in daylight

Response to Literature *Use with Student Edition page 343.*

Van Gogh's description of a café at night is found on page 339 of your textbook. Read his description again. Then write a short poem about what van Gogh saw there.

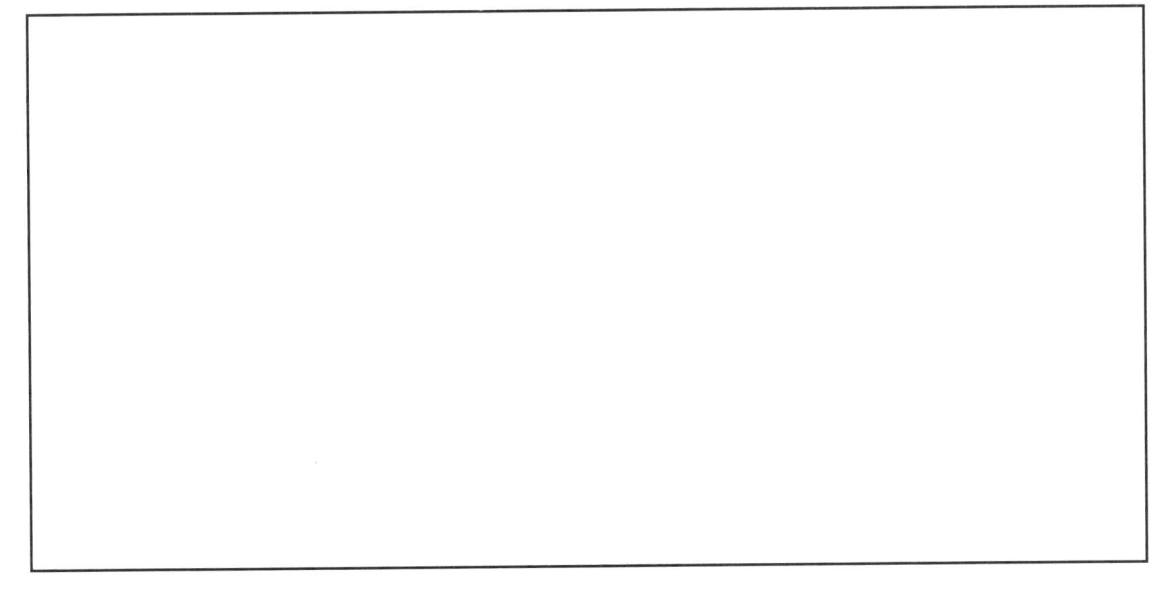

Unit 6 • Reading 2

Grammar — Expressions of Quantity: *both, either, neither*

Use with Student Edition page 344.

> **REMEMBER** Use *both* (*of the*), *either*, or *neither* when you are talking about two items. Use a plural subject and verb with *both*. Use a singular subject and verb with *either* and *neither*. However, use a plural noun and singular subject with *either of the* and *neither of the*.
> **Example:** Neither of the boys was there.
> When you name each individual person, place, or thing, use *both . . . and*, *either . . . or*, and *neither . . . nor*.

Complete the sentences with the simple present form of the verb in parentheses.

Example: Neither of the cars (work) __works__ right now.

1. Either CD (sound) _____ good to me.

2. Both of the children (want) _____ to watch the movie.

3. Both cats (lie) _____ on the bed when it's sunny.

4. Either of the horses (be) _____ ready to ride.

5. Neither of the girls (go) _____ swimming on Saturdays.

Combine the pairs of sentences using *both . . . and*, *either . . . or*, or *neither . . . nor*. Remember to use an affirmative verb with *neither . . . nor*.

Example: My brother doesn't like eggs. My sister doesn't like eggs.
__Neither my brother nor my sister likes eggs.__

6. Jane washes the dishes. Cynthia washes the dishes. (either . . . or)

7. He doesn't enjoy fishing. I don't enjoy fishing. (neither . . . nor)

8. Karen lives in Maine. Will lives in Maine. (both . . . and)

9. Frank is going to come. Isabelle is going to come. (either . . . or)

10. I'm good at swimming. Sandra is good at swimming. (both . . . and)

Name _____ Date _____

Parallel Structure *Use with Student Edition page 345.*

> **REMEMBER** Using parallel structure means that words, phrases, or clauses connected with conjunctions have a similar pattern.
> **Examples:** *The birds*, *the bees*, and *the flowers* help each other. [all plural verbs]
> Birds start *to build their nests in spring*, but they don't begin *to mate until later*. [both infinitive phrases]
> When winter *comes*, the flowers *die*. [both simple present verbs]
> The animals *were given* shelter after they *were fed*. [both clauses in passive voice]

Choose the best word or phrase to complete each sentence.

Example: We were hungry, cold, and (sleepy / felt like sleeping).

1. I have met his brother, but I (didn't meet / haven't met) his sister.
2. They love skiing and (to snowboard / snowboarding).
3. Plants need light, (to have enough water / enough water), and an appropriate climate.
4. Italy has warm beaches, great restaurants, and (Roman architecture / architecture from the Romans).

Combine the pairs of sentences with the conjunction in parentheses, making one sentence that has parallel structure.

Example: Ben is generous. Ben is honest. Ben is kind. (and)
   Ben is generous, honest, and kind.

5. Mae opened the door. Mae greeted her guests. (after)
   _____

6. We had a quiz on Friday. We had a test on Monday. (before)
   _____

7. She quit her job. She moved to New York City. She became an actor. (and)
   _____

Unit 6 • Reading 2

Grammar

Punctuation: Semicolons *Use with Student Edition page 346.*

REMEMBER You can use a semicolon instead of a period to connect two independent clauses that are closely related. A conjunctive adverb or transition often begins the clause after a semicolon.
Example: He wanted to go; however, he didn't have the time.
You can sometimes replace a coordinating conjunction with a semicolon.
Example: Jane was hurt, and she was angry, too. Jane was hurt; she was angry, too.
If groups of items in lists contain commas, semicolons may be used to separate them.

Add semicolons to the sentences below.

Example: You can have soup or salad to start; vegetables, pasta, or fish for the main course; cake or fruit for dessert; and coffee, tea, or water to drink.

1. I am going home I intend to stay there.

2. It rained all afternoon we managed to have our picnic anyway.

3. She couldn't make it to my party therefore, she brought me flowers the next day.

4. I have been to the U.S. states of California, Washington, and Oregon on the West coast Texas and New Mexico in the South and New York, Maine, and Massachusetts in the North.

5. We're going to the concert then we're going out to dinner.

6. Some colleges offer full scholarships others do not.

7. It's such a beautiful day I'll walk to the store.

8. She had very high grades in high school as a result, she got into a good university.

Name _____ Date _____

Punctuation: Colons *Use with Student Edition page 347.*

> **REMEMBER** A colon is often used to introduce a list. The clause before the colon is always an independent clause.
> **Example:** To make clam chowder you need five ingredients: clams, milk, potatoes, butter, and onions.
> NOT To make clam chowder you need: clams, milk, potatoes, butter, and onions.
> A colon can be used when an appositive, or an explanation, is introduced. The appositive may be a word, phrase, or clause.
> **Example:** He was watching his favorite movie: *The Lord of the Rings.*

Draw a line to connect each independent clause on the left with a phrase or clause on the right. Then add colons.

Example: Paul was not happy: regular attendance and class participation.

1. Course requirements are the following

2. He learned a valuable lesson

3. Only one thing was on her mind

4. It's very easy to make lemonade

5. Here are the most common girl's names

6. He finally made up his mind

7. I couldn't believe my luck

8. There is one thing you need to get

a passport.

He would major in biology.

In fact, he felt terrible.

Addison, Olivia, and Sarah.

I found my wallet that I'd lost.

Never argue with your mother.

passing the test.

Squeeze lemons into water and add sugar.

Unit 6 • Reading 2

Writing Write an Introductory Paragraph

Use with Student Edition pages 348–349.

Complete your own inverted pyramid to narrow your topic down to a single researchable question.

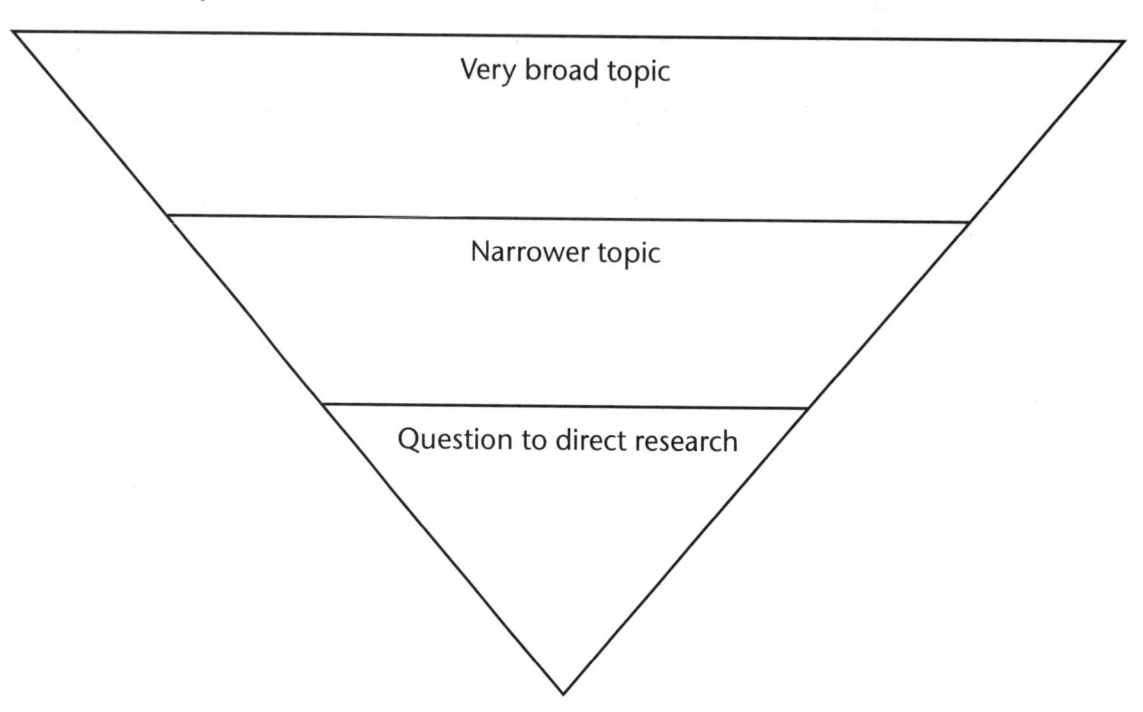

- Very broad topic
- Narrower topic
- Question to direct research

Use the Peer Review Checklist below to obtain feedback from your partner. This feedback will help you edit your final draft.

Peer Review Checklist

- [ ] Does the first sentence introduce the main research question?
- [ ] Does the paragraph explain why the topic is interesting?
- [ ] Does the paragraph explain what the report will be about?
- [ ] Is the information interesting? Did you want to find out more about the topic?
- [ ] Is punctuation used correctly?
- [ ] What changes could be made to improve the paragraph?

Name _____ Date _____

UNIT 6 — How does the sky influence us?

Reading 3: "The Moon" / "No Need to Establish a Moon Base"

Vocabulary — **Key Words** *Use with Student Edition page 351.*

Write each word in the box next to its definition.

| base | crater | lunar | ~~mine~~ | universe | voyage |

Example: ____mine____: dig into the ground in order to get gold, coal, etc.

1. _____: all of space, including the stars and planets

2. _____: a round hole in the ground made by something that has fallen or exploded

3. _____: relating to the moon

4. _____: a long trip, especially in a ship or space vehicle

5. _____: a shelter or headquarters from which an exploration can depart

Use the words in the box at the top of the page to complete the sentences.

6. The phases of the moon are known as the _____ cycle.

7. A journey across the known _____ might take trillions of years.

8. The hikers established their _____ at the bottom of the mountain.

9. Developers _____ in areas where they know coal exists.

10. The ship's captain was looking forward to the _____.

Unit 6 • Reading 3

Vocabulary: Academic Words *Use with Student Edition page 352.*

Read the paragraph below. Pay attention to the underlined Academic Words.

> NASA, the United States' National Aeronautics and Space Agency, uses telescopes and spacecraft to <u>investigate</u> our solar system and beyond. NASA scientists <u>research</u> important <u>issues</u> related to Earth, other planets, and the universe. NASA also works to <u>promote</u> public interest in its space programs. It has an excellent website with amazing photographs of the universe.

Write the Academic Words from the paragraph above next to their correct definitions.

Example: __research__ : serious study of a subject that is intended to discover new facts about it

1. _____: help something develop and be successful

2. _____: subjects or problems that people discuss

3. _____: try to find out the truth about something

Use the Academic Words from the paragraph above to complete the sentences.

4. The group deals with major social _____ like poverty and health care.

5. Alex put up flyers to _____ his new band.

6. The detective began to _____ the crime scene.

7. Sawyer is doing _____ on the way fruit flies balance in the air.

Complete the sentences with your own ideas.

Example: Forest workers promote __forest safety__.

8. Two important issues facing young people today are _____.

9. I would like to investigate _____.

10. In school I'm doing research on _____.

Unit 6 • Reading 3

Name _____ Date _____

Word Study **Acronyms** *Use with Student Edition page 353.*

REMEMBER Acronyms are created by using the first letters of a phrase, as in *LCD*, liquid crystal display. The letters are usually all capitalized and do not have periods between them.

Read each acronym. Then use a dictionary to find out what it stands for. Write the phrase in the chart.

Acronym	Words that Form Acronym
PIN	Personal Identification Number
1. NASA	
2. ATM	
3. FAQ	
4. CEO	
5. WWW	

Write the definition of each acronym. Use a dictionary if needed.

Example: UFO   <u>unidentified flying object</u>

6. ZIP (code) _____

7. TLC _____

8. Sonar _____

9. FYI _____

10. VIP _____

Unit 6 • Reading 3   **183**

Reading Strategy | **Take Notes** *Use with Student Edition page 353.*

> **REMEMBER** Taking notes helps you understand and remember new information. Think about your purpose for reading when you take notes. Scan the text and look for the information you need. Don't write in complete sentences.

Read each passage. Then answer the questions that follow.

   Java finches make great pets. They are small birds that are lively and fun to watch as they fly around in their cages. Their peeps and chirps are quieter than the piercing sound of parrots. Unlike some larger birds that need room to fly around in your house, Java finches are happy to live in their cages all the time. But owning pets is a big responsibility. Java finches need a fairly large cage. They need companionship, so you should buy a pair of them. They need fresh water for drinking and bathing and fresh finch seed. They also like fruits and vegetables.

1. Set a purpose for reading the passage. What do you hope to learn from it?

   _____

   _____

2. Take notes from the passage above.

   _____

   _____

3. What are the three most important facts in the text?

   _____

   _____

4. Write one question you have about the information presented in the passage.

   _____

   _____

5. Why is the strategy of taking notes important to understanding and remembering what you read?

   _____

   _____

Unit 6 • Reading 3

Comprehension *Use with Student Edition page 358.*

Choose the best answer for each item. Circle the letter of the correct answer.

1. Scientists believe that the Moon was originally _____.

    a. part of the sun
    b. another planet
    c. part of Earth

2. A moon base might allow astronauts to _____.

    a. study the way asteroids move
    b. study the Moon and the rest of the universe
    c. learn more about the nearby planet Venus

3. NASA wants colonies of astronauts to eventually live on the Moon for _____.

    a. as long as six weeks
    b. as long as six months
    c. as long as six years

4. Compared to manned space missions, robotic missions are _____.

    a. more dangerous
    b. much safer
    c. about equally safe

5. The two authors disagree _____.

    a. about how to explore space
    b. about how many space missions to fly
    c. if we should explore space further

Extension *Use with Student Edition page 359.*

Several countries have launched satellites in the last 50 years. Research five countries and tell when they launched their first satellite.

Country	Date of first satellite launch
United States	January 31, 1958

Unit 6 • Reading 3

Grammar — More Transitions *Use with Student Edition page 360.*

REMEMBER Transitions help you make smoother transitions in your writing. They can be used to add information (*moreover, furthermore, in addition*); to contrast two ideas (*instead, rather, alternatively*); to show cause and effect (*as a result, hence, accordingly*); to clarify (*for example, to illustrate, that is*); to emphasize a point (*for this reason, indeed, in fact*); and to summarize ideas (*in summary, finally, in conclusion*). Transitions begin sentences or clauses and are followed by commas.

Complete the essay with appropriate transitions. More than one answer is possible.

Why the Voting Age Should Be Lowered
by Jen Maddocks

The voting age should be lowered to 16 so that younger people's voices can be heard.

1. _____, younger people would become more active in politics.

2. _____, I believe there is a double standard for young people. We have adult responsibilities without the rights of adults. 3. _____, 16-year-olds have jobs and pay taxes, but cannot take part in electing our officials.

4. _____, 16-year-olds would contribute more to society if they had the right to vote. 5. _____, their votes might change laws that affect them. 6. _____, young people have a unique perspective that needs to be represented. 7. _____, kids have an interest in laws having to do with schools.

8. _____, most youths want to be part of the democratic process of the nation. I believe that lowering the voting age will give 16-year-olds a constructive and democratic channel for making their views known.

Name _____ Date _____

Present and Past Progressive *Use with Student Edition page 361.*

> **REMEMBER** The present progressive shows an action in progress now or in the future. Form the present progressive with *is*, *am*, or *are* and a present participle. The past progressive shows an action in progress at some time in the past. Form the past progressive with *was* or *were* and the present participle. To show that the action was interrupted, use the simple past with the past progressive. The adverb *while* with the clause in the present progressive implies a duration of time; the adverb *when* with the clause in the simple past implies a point in time.

Underline the verb(s) in each sentence. Write whether the action is in the *present*, *past*, or *future*.

Example: I'm going to Morocco on vacation this summer. _____future_____

1. I was taking a bath when the phone rang. _____

2. She's cooking dinner right now. _____

3. We're staying at a hotel next weekend. _____

4. At 5:30, I was washing the dishes. _____

Complete each sentence below with the present progressive, past progressive, or simple past of the verb in parentheses.

Example: He _'s working_ (work) on his project this afternoon.

5. What _____ you _____ (do) after work today?

6. What _____ you _____ (do) when I _____ (call) you yesterday?

7. I can't talk right now. I _____ (shop) for some presents.

8. She _____ (not watch) the movie last night. She _____ (cooking) instead.

Unit 6 • Reading 3

Grammar — Parentheses, Brackets, and Ellipses

Use with Student Edition page 362.

> **REMEMBER** Parentheses (( )) can show extra information or set off an abbreviation.
> **Example:** The states (New York and South Carolina) voted against the amendment.
> Brackets ([ ]) can show changes made to original text.
> **Example:** [They] were unhappy with the conditions and voted against the amendment.
> Ellipses (…) can indicate a word or phrase missing from original text.
> **Example:** The states … voted against the amendment.

Read the following sentences, adding parentheses where necessary.

Example: He works for the United Nations High Commission on Refugees (UNHCR).

1. The boys Tom, Dick, and Harry collected the money.

2. The New York Stock Exchange NYSE is closed for the holiday.

3. Use parentheses to set off an appositive another name for a noun.

Rewrite each sentence, using brackets with the boldfaced words and ellipses instead of the underlined phrase.

Example: **Dr. Smith and Dr. Jones** gave a talk at the museum on dinosaurs.

[The professors] gave a talk … on dinosaurs.

4. **Saul's** paper describing plant life on Mars was interesting.

5. His opinion that the economy will improve is not widely held by **the other economists**.

6. **The scientists** completed, with the help of others, their research.

Name _____ Date _____

Quoting Sources *Use with Student Edition page 363.*

> **REMEMBER** When quoting sources in a paper, you can use direct or reported speech. Direct speech is introduced with a reporting verb, often in present tense, such as *says*, *contends*, or *argues*, and is set off with quotation marks. Quotation marks are not used with reported speech. A block quotation is used to quote three or more sentences. Block quotations are introduced with a colon, indented, and don't have quotation marks.

Read the passage below. Follow the instructions for quoting sources.

> **The National Air and Space Museum**
> by Stan Keeger
> The National Air and Space Museum (NASM), which is part of the Smithsonian Institution, is its most popular attraction. It is conveniently located in Washington, D.C. It holds the largest collection of historic aircraft and spacecraft in the world. It is also a center for research into the history of aviation and spaceflight. Almost all space and aircraft on display are originals. It is a fascinating place to visit.

Example: Quote the first sentence using reported speech.

<u>Keeger states that the NASM is the Smithsonian's most popular attraction.</u>

1. Quote the second sentence using direct speech.

   _____

2. Quote the third, fourth, and fifth sentences using a block quotation.

   _____

   _____

   _____

3. Quote the third sentence using reported speech.

   _____

4. Quote the fourth sentence using direct speech.

   _____

5. Quote the last sentence using reported speech.

   _____

Writing — Include Quotations and Citations

Use with Student Edition pages 364–365.

Complete your own source chart for a paragraph that includes quotations and citations.

Quotation	Source

Use the Peer Review Checklist below to obtain feedback from your partner. This feedback will help you edit your final draft.

Peer Review Checklist

- ☐ Is the main idea clearly presented?
- ☐ Is the main idea supported with details?
- ☐ Are quotations and citations included?
- ☐ Do quotations flow smoothly within paragraphs?
- ☐ Is a "Works Consulted" list provided?
- ☐ What changes could be made to improve the paragraph?

Name _____ Date _____

Writing Workshop Use with Student Edition pages 370–376.

Organize your ideas in the graphic organizer below.

> I.
>   A.
>   B.
> II.
>   A.
>   B.
> III.
>   A.
>   B.
> IV.
>   A.
>   B.
> V.
>   A.
>   B.

Use the Peer Review Checklist below to obtain feedback from your partner. This feedback will help you edit your final draft.

Peer Review Checklist

- ☐ Was the topic clearly introduced in the first paragraph?
- ☐ Was the information supported with details and facts?
- ☐ Did the writer show a thorough understanding of the topic?
- ☐ Did the writer use transitions to show a logical sequence of ideas?
- ☐ Did the concluding paragraph sum up the main points in a memorable way?
- ☐ What changes could be made to improve the essay?

Learning Log *Use after completing page 376.*

Underline each vocabulary item you know and can use well. Review and practice any you haven't underlined. Underline them when you know them well.

Literary Words	Key Words	Academic Words	
myth	lunar	compatible	interpretation
personification	voyage	instructed	visible
stanza	craters	job	investigate
rhyme	base	phase	issues
rhyme scheme	universe	analyze	promote
	mine	image	research

Put a check by the skills you can perform well. Review and practice any you haven't checked off. Check them off when you can perform them well.

Skills	I can . . .
Word Study	☐ recognize and use lexical sets. ☐ recognize and spell words with a long *i*. ☐ recognize words that form acronyms.
Reading Strategies	☐ analyze text structure and elements of poetry. ☐ read for enjoyment. ☐ take notes.
Grammar	☐ use prepositions and antecedent/pronoun agreement. ☐ use punctuation, semicolons, and colons. ☐ use expressions of quantity. ☐ use parallel structure. ☐ use capitalization, hyphens, and dashes. ☐ use parentheses, brackets, and ellipses; quote sources. ☐ use transitions. ☐ use present and past progressive.
Writing	☐ write an introductory paragraph for a research report. ☐ write a paragraph using paraphrases and citations. ☐ write a paragraph using quotations and citations. ☐ write a research report.

Name _____ Date _____

Test Preparation

Test 1

DIRECTIONS
Read this selection. Then answer the questions that follow it.

Chinese New Year

1   Everyone is invited to celebrate the Year of the Tiger in Chinatown on February 19 and 20. The two-day event is fun for the whole family.

2   Friday the festival starts with a fashion show. Local musicians will play traditional Chinese tunes in front of the Hong Kong Market. Dancers will take the stage at 5:00 p.m. Children are invited to make tiger masks in honor of the Year of the Tiger.

3   On Saturday, visitors will enjoy the traditional dragon dance. Again, bands will entertain visitors throughout the day. Chefs from several restaurants in Chinatown will offer free samples of food. The evening will end with a huge fireworks display.

1 According to the selection, what is the first event?
   A Musicians on stage
   B The dragon dance
   C A fashion show
   D Children making masks

2 Where would you most likely find this passage?
   A In a newspaper
   B On a highway billboard
   C In a restaurant menu
   D On a map of Chinatown

3 When will the dancers perform?
   A Saturday at 10:00 a.m.
   B During the dragon dance
   C After the fireworks display
   D Friday at 5:00 p.m.

Test 2

DIRECTIONS
Read this selection. Then answer the questions that follow it.

Asteroids and Comets

1   Asteroids are part of the solar system. They are pieces of rock and metal. They can be very small or hundreds of kilometers wide. Most of the asteroids in our solar system orbit the sun between Mars and Jupiter.

2   Scientists believe that a big asteroid fell to Earth 65 million years ago. It hit in what is now Mexico. The asteroid was about ten kilometers wide. The asteroid was moving so fast that it made a hole almost 200 kilometers wide. Scientists believe the asteroid caused an explosion that sparked huge fires. The dust and smoke made a dark cloud and blocked sunlight for months. Many kinds of plants and animals probably died.

3   One of the most beautiful sights in the night sky is a comet. A comet is a mass of ice, frozen gases, and dust. Comets orbit the sun. You can see a comet when it is near the sun. The sun heats up the comet. This causes the ice to turn into a cloud of gases with a long tail. Comets do not make their own light. They <u>reflect</u>, or throw back, the sun's light. The brightest comets can be seen only every ten to twelve years.

---

1 According to the article, asteroids —
  A orbit Earth
  B orbit the sun
  C orbit Jupiter
  D orbit the Moon

2 Which sentence in paragraph 3 is an opinion?
  A *One of the most beautiful sights in the night sky is a comet.*
  B *They reflect, or throw back, the sun's light.*
  C *A comet is a mass of ice, frozen gases, and dust.*
  D *You can see a comet when it is near the sun.*

3 In paragraph 3, what words help the reader know what *reflect* means?
  A sun's light
  B throw back
  C make their own light
  D can be seen

4 Paragraph 2 is mainly about —
  A the cause of an asteroid falling to Earth
  B What scientist believe happened when an asteroid hit Earth in the past
  C the size of an asteroid that hit Mexico
  D the animals and plants that died when an asteroid hit earth

Test 3

DIRECTIONS
Read this selection. Then answer the questions that follow it.

Pictures in the Stars

1. Ray tapped his foot as he waited for the doors to open. "I hope this doesn't take too long," he thought. "This stuff is boring." Just then the doors to the planetarium opened and he followed his classmates inside. He looked up and was amazed at the images on the dome-shaped ceiling.

2. "Welcome, students," the guide said. "Today we are going to learn about common constellations. As you know, constellations are patterns of stars. These patterns include the stars that we know best, the ones closest to us. Some of these stars are in patterns that look like people or animals, so people have given them names. Can anyone name one of the best-known constellations?"

3. Ray raised his hand. "One of the best-known constellations is the Big Dipper," Ray said.

4. "That's right. It's called the Big Dipper because it looks like a cup with a long handle. But did you know that the Big Dipper is not a true constellation?" The students shook their heads.

5. "The Big Dipper is not a true constellation because it is part of another constellation called Ursa Major, the Great Bear. The Big Dipper's handle is also the bear's tail." The guide pointed out the image of the Great Bear on the screen above them. Then he changed the screen and asked the students to look for three stars in the pattern of a belt.

6. The guide continued, "Another well-known constellation is Orion. Orion is a character in an ancient Greek myth, or story. He was a great hunter. On a clear night, look for the three stars that make his belt. Once you have found his belt, it is easy to see his right thigh and shoulders." The guide pointed out other constellations. Then he gave each student a booklet to help them find the constellations at home.

7. Ray could hardly wait for the sun to set. He wondered whether he would be able to see all the constellations in the booklet. When night finally came, he went outside with his dad and started searching the sky.

Test Preparation

1 Which sentence BEST shows how Ray feels about going to the planetarium at the beginning of the story?

A *Ray tapped his foot as he waited for the doors to open.*

B *"I hope this doesn't take too long," he thought.*

C *He looked up and was amazed at the images on the dome-shaped ceiling.*

D *When night finally came, he went outside with his dad and started searching the sky.*

2 Paragraph 5 is mainly about —

A Orion
B Ursa Major
C the Big Dipper
D Ray's excitement

3 In paragraph 1, what words help the reader know what *planetarium* means?

A images on the dome-shaped ceiling
B the doors
C looked up and was amazed
D opened and he followed his classmates inside

4 Look at the graphic organizer at the bottom of the page. Which of the following belongs in the box for Event 3?

A The guide described the Big Dipper.
B Ray raised his hand and answered the question.
C The guide told the students about the constellation named Orion.
D The guide explained that the Big Dipper was one of the best-known constellations.

5 According to the selection, if you can find the three stars in the pattern of a belt you can —

A find the constellation Ursa Major
B find the constellation Scorpio
C find the constellation Orion
D find the constellation Ursa Minor

Event 1	Event 2	Event 3	Event 4
The guide showed the students the Big Dipper.	The guide explained that the Big Dipper was part of Ursa Major.		Ray and his father went outside to find constellations.

196   Test Preparation

Name _____ Date _____

Visual Literacy: Smithsonian American Art Museum *Use with Student Edition pages 378–379.*

Learning to Look

Look at *Orion in December* by Charles Burchfield on page 379 in your Student Edition. The artist felt inspired to paint *Orion in December* after looking out of his bedroom window on a winter night. Pretend you are looking out of a bedroom window. How would you paint the same scene?

Example: I would paint a winter night in December with snow . . .

_____
_____
_____
_____
_____
_____

Interpretation

Look at *The Eclipse* by Alma Thomas on page 378 in your Student Edition. If this painting could give off a sound, what would it be? Explain your answer.

Example: The sound would be loud and made with drums.

_____
_____
_____
_____
_____

Compare & Contrast

Look again at *Orion in December* and *The Eclipse* again. Use these two artworks to complete the diagram below. Describe each piece of art in the outer sections of the diagram. Then list the similarities between the two paintings in the center where the two circles overlap.

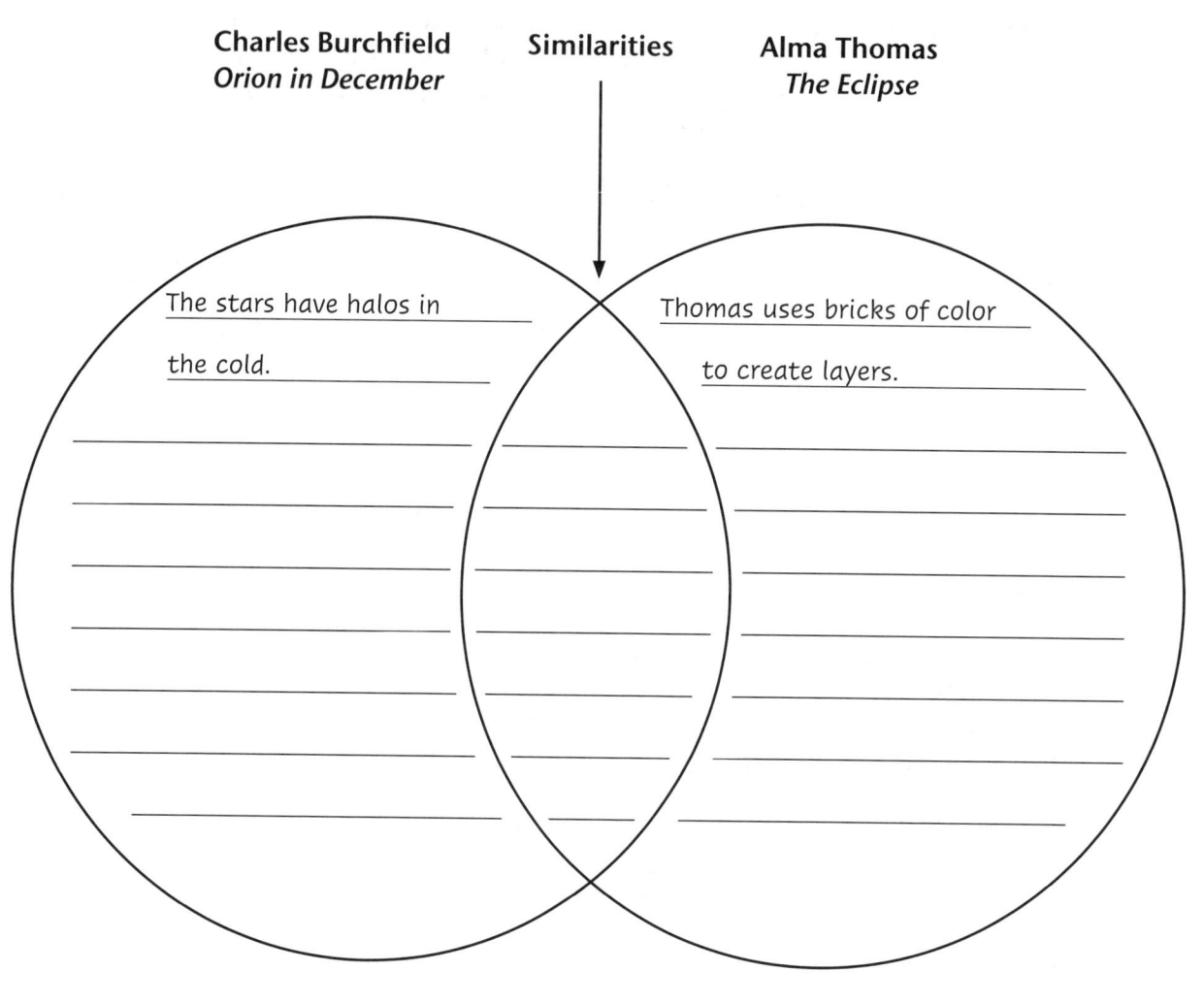

Charles Burchfield
Orion in December

Similarities

Alma Thomas
The Eclipse

The stars have halos in the cold.

Thomas uses bricks of color to create layers.

Editing and Proofreading Marks

To:	Use This Mark	Example:
add something	∧	We ate rice, bean^s and corn.
delete something	߷	We ate rice, beans, and corns.
close space	⌒	We ⌒ ate rice, beans, and corn.
start a new paragraph	¶	¶ We ate rice, beans, and corn.
add a comma	⋏	We ate rice, beans and corn.
add a period	⊙	We ate rice, beans, and corn⊙
switch letters or words	∽	We ate rice, baens, and corn.
change to a capital letter	$\underline{\underline{a}}$	we ate rice, beans, and corn.
change to a lowercase letter	⁄	WE ate rice, beans, and corn.
let the marked text stand	(stet)	We ate rice, beans, and corn. (stet)

Additional Editing and Proofreading Practice

Read the paragraph below carefully. Look for mistakes in spelling, punctuation, and grammar. Mark the mistakes with proofreader's marks. Then rewrite the paragraph correctly on the lines below.

> Everyone in the family was excited for our trip. my sister was home from school. I had not seen her in more than six months. on the day before we left, we had to pack our bags I packed my toothbrush a summer hat and five pairs of socks. I put them into my large backpack, Then I choosed two warm shirts and one light one. I also packed a smallest brown bag just for the car ride. it was a gift from my grandmother. I put two books in the bag so i could read them on the way to the cabin My parents told me to bring a bottle for water, too. I wanted to bring my cat Buster, but he had to stay home. Cats are not allowed to stay on the cabin with families. But even without buster, we had a wonderful time.

Additional Editing and Proofreading Practice

201

Edit and Proofread

Read the paragraph below carefully. Look for mistakes in spelling, punctuation, and grammar. Mark the mistakes with proofreader's marks. Then rewrite the paragraph correctly on the lines below.

Last summer, I go away to a nearby college as part of a program for high school students. I took one class in chemistry and one in english. The classes was harder than my high school classes, but I worked hard and did well. the students in my program all stayd in the same dormitory We played soccer in the hallway! The athletic field was Nearby, but it wasn't close enough. Visiting the city was fun, too. I had never had a chance to exploar such a big city on my own. I road my bike at musuems and shops, and my new friends and I walked on the waterfront at night. I enjoyed studying for classes and working with professors But I enjoyed my new freedom even more.

202   Additional Editing and Proofreading Practice

Edit and Proofread

Read the paragraph carefully. Look for mistakes in spelling, punctuation, and grammar. Mark the mistakes with proofreader's marks. Then rewrite the paragraph correctly on the lines below.

> Juan hates it when his mother orders him around. Her latest instruction is simple: She said Son, clean your room." So Juan decided to alfebetize his music collection. He picked up three cds that had falen behind his desk. They were by his favorite singor, Prince. He realized that he had never actually lisened to any of them before. They had fallen behind the desk the day he bought them. Juan decided maybee his mom was right. maybe it wasnt such a bad idea after all to be neet and organized.

Additional Editing and Proofreading Practice

Edit and Proofread

Read the paragraph below carefully. Look for mistakes in spelling, punctuation, and grammar. Mark the mistakes with proofreader's marks. Then rewrite the paragraph correctly on the lines below.

During the summer, several students from the local high school had a fun volunteer expereince. The New Hope Clinic, who provides free medical consultation to neighborhood families, is located near the school. One of the students' tasks was to help make patients feel at home The students would offers refreshments to the Patients and engage them in conversation to make them comfortable. When pateints couldn't read or write, the students would assist them. Each student also spent a day shadowing one of the nurses, which were happy to provide guidance. The nurses prepare the patients for docter visits, take down patient informatoin, and provide first aid to patients that need it. One of our students, Enrique Martin, stayed for an extra week at the end of the summer. He followed Dr. dalek around the office, watching him treat patients. Enrique has decided to study medicine next year at college

Name _____ Date _____

Edit and Proofread

Read the paragraph below carefully. Look for mistakes in spelling, punctuation, and grammar. Mark the mistakes with proofreader's marks. Then rewrite the paragraph correctly on the lines below.

> I have been going to the park every day to practice tennis. I play on the varsity team, but everyone needs practice. One day, after I had been Practicing for about an hour, I saw my grandad sitting at one of the picnic benches. He was sitting all alone, and he looked sad. After I finished practicing, I walked over to his bench and asked how he was doing. Granddad just grinned. "Do you play chess" he asked. I has played a few times. He asked if I wanted to play a game. we played three games of chess that afternoon. I came close to beeting him once but he smiled and captured one of my pieces right away After our last game I said goodbye and walked back to the tennis cort.

Additional Editing and Proofreading Practice

Edit and Proofread

Read the paragraph below carefully. Look for mistakes in spelling, punctuation, and grammar. Mark the mistakes with proofreader's marks. Then rewrite the paragraph correctly on the lines.

> This weak the eighth grade class took a field trip to the space Exploration museum. Hannah had been to the museum several times she really enjoyed the exhibits. She dreamed of growing up to become an astronaut. The group was passing a Display about Goddard's rockets when her phone rang Her mother was calling her. Hannah looked around for a place to anser the phone in private. She went to a hallway nearby so she wouldn't disturb any one. Our teacher got upset that Hannah left the group.